THE GOLDEN LEGEND SERIES

THE QUEST OF THE BEAST

**The Questing Beast—an artist's impression,
based on a contemporary illustration**

THE QUEST
OF THE BEAST

FROM SIR THOMAS MALORY'S
'MORTE D'ARTHUR'
AND OTHER SOURCES

BY BRIAN KENNEDY COOKE

*ILLUSTRATIONS IN THE TEXT FROM
'TAVOLA ROTONDA' (COD. PAL. 556)
BY COURTESY OF THE NATIONAL LIBRARY,
FLORENCE*

*FRONTISPIECE BY D. S. CAMMELL
after the design by Mary Colley*

EDMUND WARD (PUBLISHERS) LTD
194-200 BISHOPSGATE, LONDON EC2

First published by
EDMUND WARD (PUBLISHERS) LIMITED
194–200 Bishopsgate, London EC2

Printed in England by
ADLARD AND SON LIMITED
London and Dorking

CONTENTS

LIST OF ILLUSTRATIONS

Facing page

PREFACE

THE KNIGHTS OF THE ROUND TABLE are on the whole a homogeneous collection. In origin they may be French or Roman-British, Scottish, Irish, or Cornish, but they have a strong family likeness and, whether agreeing or quarrelling with each other, they all seem to speak the same language. In character they range from the wholly good (Sir Galahad) to the wholly bad (Sir Mordred), and the standard by which such qualities are determined is a constant one. Even outside the great fellowship the same standard is applied. Sir Lancelot and his fellows wholly condemned a villain like Sir Breuse-sans-Pité, but they understood him. They also knew precisely what to expect of the 'Saracen' knights that crossed their path: that, not being Christians, they would be closely associated with the devil, would have virtually no code of honour, and would be liable to emit a most unpleasant smell when their heads were cut off. And the Saracens faithfully lived up to these expectations.

Into this world, so straightforward in spite of magicians and haunted forests, there comes a knight of Babylon with his mysterious but apparently western wife and their three sons. The parents and the two younger sons accept Christianity soon after they arrive in Britain (the mother may indeed have been Christian before) and conform at all points, or nearly all, to the prevailing standard on their comparatively rare appearances. But the eldest son, Sir Palomides, not only rejects Christianity for many years but repeatedly does the unexpected. His good as well as his bad actions fail to keep to the rules. He is continually a puzzle to his companions, and he remains a puzzle to us. Tristram without Iseult, Lancelot without the

Lady of the Lake and Guinevere, would be mere types, as many of the other knights are. But Palomides is a real character—perhaps the only complex character in the stories.

With him is associated a remarkable animal called the Questing Beast. In the surviving legends Palomides has a beginning and two mutually contradictory ends, while his Beast has a beginning and no end. In Malory's *Morte d'Arthur* Palomides has only a middle and one end; and the middle consists almost entirely of a long series of battles and tournaments from which the appearances of the Questing Beast provide a welcome but rare diversion. Yet even in Malory the hints of a strange unorthodox character are to be found. In the prose Tristram and in the work of Rusticiano da Pisa there is a good deal more material and the character is more firmly drawn.

In making this book, I have drastically condensed the narrative of Malory, adapted thereto a number of passages from the other sources, and supplied what I thought was needed to develop and round off the story of the Knight and the Beast. Whether I have succeeded in delineating adequately the interesting and intricate character that I see in Sir Palomides, the reader must judge.

Charlemagne and the Book

IN the history of Charlemagne that is at Aix-la-Chappelle it is told how the Emperor went to Beauregard Castle, where was a bronze statue of Sir Galahad; and there too he saw all the pictures and inscriptions that told of the great deeds of Sir Galahad, Sir Tristram, Sir Lancelot, and Sir Palomides. And Charlemagne marvelled greatly at King Arthur, and deemed him but a poor-spirited king for that with four such knights he had not conquered the whole world.

'Nay, Sire,' said one that stood by, 'King Arthur was no coward; and other things there be for a king to do beside making war in realms that are not his. And as for those knights, Sir Galahad was set upon the Grail Quest, and Sir Lancelot and Sir Tristram destroyed themselves with earthly loves.'

'And what of Palomides?' said the Emperor. But at this time there was none to answer him, for the man that spoke was there no longer.

So there in an abbey the Emperor found the swords of Sir Tristram and Sir Palomides. And all they that were with the Emperor held that the sword of Palomides was better than the sword of Tristram. So Charlemagne kept the sword of Palomides for himself, and the sword of Tristram he gave to Ogier the Dane. But this Ogier, that was a mighty man enough, found that sword too long and too heavy, that he might not wield it. And so he made a smith to shorten it; therefore was it called Cortaine.

And when the Emperor was in his old age, he made a

clerk to read him the adventures of the four knights whenas he sat at meat. And ever the Emperor leaned to Palomides, of whom little was written; but of the others much was written.

And on a day the Emperor rose from his seat and said: 'Verily I deem Palomides a better knight than Lancelot and a better man.'

And all they that sat at meat with him were astonied, for all the books said that Sir Lancelot was the best knight of the world, save it were his son, Sir Galahad, and after him Sir Tristram. Yet none dared answer the Emperor.

Then on a sudden the Emperor was aware that there stood before him the man of Beauregard, and in his hand a book. And the Emperor said: 'Ha! Art thou come again that would not answer my question? What of Palomides?'

'Thou, Sire, hast made bold to answer it,' said he. 'Yet what know ye of Palomides, save what is writ in your clerk's book? And little enough is there writ to tell what manner of man he was.'

'That is truth,' said the Emperor.

'Now take this book,' said the man, 'and learn the story of Palomides. And then may ye say, if ye will, which was the better and which the worse. Yet, an ye be wise as all men think you, ye will not make a judgment that is God's to make.'

And so saying he vanished from the Emperor's sight.

I

The Birth of the Questing Beast

THERE was a lord in Babylon that hight Esclabor, and he had to wife a fair lady and a wise that had come by mischance to Babylon when but a child. For it chanced on a day as she played by the sea-shore in Ireland that there came a Saracen ship, and the Saracens went out of the ship to burn and slay and take what booty they might. But the men of that part encountered with the Saracens and slew many of them so that the rest were fain to make what speed they might back to their ship. And no booty they got and no profit; save only they carried with them the young damsel. And her name was Etain.

Now the King of Babylon was under bond to send a tribute to the Emperor of Rome every fifth year; and the custom was that he sent with the tribute one of his lords to abide in Rome with the Emperor till that the next tribute was paid. And when they drew lots among the lords the lot fell upon Esclabor, and he was exceeding heavy. And he thought how he might send some other in his stead. But his wife came to him and said: 'Why does my lord grieve?'

'Because,' he said, 'I am sent into a far country, and I know not when I shall return.'

'Ye shall not return,' said she, 'but grieve not for that. For much honour shall ye and your sons find in those far countries. Therefore rouse you and make ready, and take all your goods that ye may. And I and our three sons will go with you.'

So when the day was come, Lord Esclabor and his wife and his three sons, with the King's tribute and a great company of knights and squires, set forth for Rome. Now of the three sons of Esclabor, the first was called Palomides; and he was ten years old and so goodly a child that all men marvelled to behold him. And his two brethren were named Safere and Segwarides.

And when they were come to Rome, the Emperor received them well, and so they abode in the Palace. And the Emperor had a young lion that he loved much, and the Emperor took no heed of the lords that besought him to put it away; for it was nigh full-grown, and they feared it would do him a mischief. And on a day, when the Emperor played with his lion, suddenly the lion sprang upon him and would have devoured him. And they that were by wot not what they should do, for they were sore afeared of the lion. But Esclabor drew his sword, and ran upon the lion and seized it by the main and thrust the sword into its throat, and so saved the Emperor. And from that day the Emperor showed him much favour and had him ever in his counsels.

And the lords and knights of the court were exceeding jealous of Esclabor and began to hate him sore. For they deemed it shame that a stranger should be preferred before them. And so they took counsel together to slay him. And on a day when Esclabor was to go on a journey they laid an ambush for him. But Etain, who was ware of their evil intent by her arts, held Esclabor in converse on this thing and on that, so that the hour passed when he should have ridden forth.

Now it chanced that the Emperor's nephew, that hight

Gratian, rode by the way that the ambush was laid; and he had but one squire with him for he rode to a tryst with a lady that he loved greatly. And when he came to the ambush it was dark, and the knights that were there deemed that he was Esclabor; and so they rose all together and fell upon him and slew him. And the squire escaped and fled back to Rome. So when those knights saw him that they had slain they were sore afraid, and they drew them away quickly, each to his castle, to wait what would befall.

And when at last Esclabor had answered all his wife's saying and came to take his leave of the Emperor, it was full night. And he found with the Emperor a messenger that had but then come from the west. And he told the Emperor of the young King Arthur that had of late been crowned in the country of Logres, and how he had pulled the sword out of the stone and other marvels.

And with that came the squire of Gratian, and told how his master had been set upon and slain by divers knights of Rome. And the Emperor was passing wroth and vowed a great vengeance upon all those knights. And then he summoned all them that were at the court that he might know who had done this thing.

But the Lady Etain craved hearing of the Emperor, and when she was come she spake as follows

'My lord, right kind and gracious have ye been to my husband and to me and to our children. And now I know this deed hath been done, not for any evil will towards you, but they mistook your nephew for my lord. And if ye make war upon so many knights, ye will ruin all this land. And we are strangers here, and they could not endure the kindness that ye showed to the Lord Esclabor above all others. Wherefore

I crave this last boon. Let us depart in peace out of your palace, and pardon these your knights that knew not what they did, and ye shall have peace in your days. As for us, we will go seek this new king that ye have but now heard tell of, and I doubt not that we shall find kindness with him as we have with you.'

Then the Emperor was silent a long time, for he would not these knights should go free; and yet at the last he deemed that the lady spoke wisdom. So he granted that it should be as she said.

And on the morrow the Emperor made a proclamation in all as she had said, and to Esclabor he gave many gifts, and so they departed out of that country. And when they came to the coast they took ship; and after many days landed upon the shores of Northumberland. And there they encountered with King Pellinore, that was king of Galis. And this King Pellinore had a quest. For he sought a strange beast that wandered through the world, and he might not ever leave it while he was on live.[1]

So while they were lodged with the King there came in Merlin, and sat him down at the board. And King Pellinore looked ever on the boy Palomides, and his heart yearned towards him as though he had been his heir.

Then said Merlin to King Pellinore: 'Why look ye so on that lad?'

'In faith I know not,' said King Pellinore, 'but meseemeth he should be near of kin to me, though I know not how this could be.'

'No kin is he of yours,' said Merlin, 'but he it is that shall follow that beast that now ye follow. For ye shall never

[1] alive.

achieve it for all your striving and the might of your hands.'

'That may well be,' said King Pellinore, 'for never yet did I come nigh unto it. And yet never may I leave that quest for long. But, since ye know that I shall achieve it not, know ye also if the boy shall achieve it?'

But Merlin would say no more that day. Only he told Lord Esclabor that his son should be made knight. And so the Lord Esclabor besought King Pellinore that he would make Sir Palomides knight and so he did.

And that night the Lady Etain came secretly to Merlin and said: 'What is this beast that shall be my son's quest? And must he ever pursue a monster, nor ever win worship in tournaments and battles as is the way of good knights?'

'Nay, lady, much worship shall he win,' said Merlin, 'but ever and anon he must return to the quest of this beast, as now doth King Pellinore. And this beast is called the Questing Beast; but some call it Glatisant for the noise that it makes.'

'But what manner of Beast is this?' said Etain, 'And wherefore must noble knights pursue it?'

'As for that,' said Merlin, 'some pursue it for this cause, and some for that. But the begetting of the beast was in this wise. The daughter of King Ypomenus set great love upon her brother, but he would have none of her. And for very grief she ran out to the wild places to slay herself. And there met with her a fair youth that stayed her from her purpose and vowed to help her if she would lie with him. And so she did; and then she gan greatly to love this youth and to hate her brother. But the youth was Satan in disguise, and at his bidding she bore false witness against her brother so that he was condemned to death.

'Then was it allowed the maiden to choose the form of his

death; and she decreed that her brother be thrown to dogs that had been kept seven days fasting. And so it was done. But ere he died the prince did prophesy that his sister would bring forth a monster in whose belly should ever be the sound of dogs barking as a memory of his shameful death. And soon thereafter the Princess was brought to bed of this beast that the devil had gotten upon her. And her maidens died of horror at the sight thereof. And the King her father, suspecting some evil thing, put her to the torture till at last she confessed all. And then her father commanded that she be strangled. But the beast escaped out of the court, and sithen[1] it wanders on the face of the earth.'

'This is an evil tale,' said Etain, 'and what evil hath my son done that this foul quest should be given him?'

'No evil hath he done as yet,' said Merlin, 'and though the beast was foully conceived that doth not befoul the quest of it. For to every knight is given the quest that him fits. But only the noble knight achieves it.'

And then Merlin departed suddenly, none knew whither. And thereafter the Lord Esclabor and his wife and his sons took leave of King Pellinore and set out again upon their journey. And at the last they came to the court of King Arthur that was at Caerleon at that time.

And right nobly did King Arthur receive them; and to Lord Esclabor and Lady Etain he gave a castle and lands. And it was agreed between them that at the feast of Pentecost next following Esclabor and his three sons should be baptized. But Etain had been baptized ere she came into Babylon. Also the King would make Esclabor a knight of the Table Round, but Esclabor said:

[1] since then.

'Nay, Sire, for ye need not old knights but young, and at this time I am past the days of my might. But and if on a day ye deem my son, Palomides, that is newly made knight, worthy of honour, let him then have my place.'

'Right now shall he have it,' said the king, 'although he be not yet christened. For I wot that he shall prove full worthy.'

So then Sir Palomides was made to sit at the Round Table and many knights deemed it strange that a knight untried and unchristened should sit among them, and some spake openly against it. But Sir Palomides spake no word, but kept his own counsel.

II

The Quest Begins

Now when the day of Pentecost was come, Esclabor and his two sons, Safere and Segwarides came to the Cathedral to be baptized, but Palomides came not nor could any find him. And the king was wroth, and began to swear a great oath that none should have baptism till that Palomides were found.

And with that came Merlin, and cried upon the king right hotly.

'What is this folly,' said Merlin, 'that ye will deny baptism to three that would have it because ye cannot find one that would have it not? Let make christen these that are here, and let be these great oaths that do no honour neither to God nor to thy kingship.'

'Where is Palomides?' said the king.

'Thou shalt not at this time find him,' said Merlin, 'and therefore seek him not.'

And from these words the king wot well that Merlin had seen Palomides; but he said no more at that time, but bade the Bishop christen those that were there. And when the service was done, then the king said that he would go hunting in the forest. And there he chased an hart so hard that on a sudden his horse fell dead. And then his squire bade the king rest there where he was, and he would get him another horse.

So the king sat down by a fountain and there he fell in

great thought. And as he sat there him thought that he heard a noise of hounds to the sum of thirty. And with that the king saw come towards him the strangest beast that ever he saw or heard of. So this beast went to the well and drank; and the noise was in the beast's belly. But all the while the beast drank there was no noise in the beast's belly. And therewith the beast departed with a great noise, whereof the king had great marvel. And so he was in great thought, and therewith he fell on sleep.

Right so there came a knight on foot unto Arthur, and said: 'Knight full of thought and sleepy, tell me if thou sawest any strange beast pass this way.'

'Such an one saw I,' said King Arthur, 'that is past nigh two mile. What would ye with that beast?'

'Sir, I have followed that beast long and killed mine horse. So would God I had another to follow my quest.'

Right so came one with the king's horse. And when the knight saw the horse he prayed the king to give him the horse. 'For,' said he, 'I have followed this quest a twelve-month. And either I shall achieve it or bleed of the best blood in my body.'

'Sir knight,' said the king, 'leave that quest and suffer me to have it and I will follow it another twelve month.'

'Ah, fool,' said the knight, 'it is in vain thy desire. For it shall never be achieved but by me while I am on live.'

And therewith he went unto the king's horse and mounted into the saddle, and said: 'Gramercy, for this horse is mine own.'

'Well,' said the king, 'thou mayest take my horse by force; but, an I might prove it, I would test whether thou wert better worthy to have him than I.'

When the knight heard him say so, he said: 'Seek me here when thou wilt, and here nigh this well thou shalt find me'—and so passed on his way.

Then the king sat in a study, and bade his men fetch another horse as fast as they might.

Right so came by him Merlin, like a child of fourteen years of age, and saluted the king and asked him why he was so pensive.

'I may well be pensive,' said the king, 'for I have seen the marvelloust sight that ever I saw.'

'That know I well,' said Merlin, 'as well as thyself and of all thy thoughts. But thou art a fool to take thought for it that will not amend thee. Also I know wherefore thou camest into this forest.'

'How shouldst thou know it? For thou art not so old of years to know these things,' said Arthur, 'I will not believe thee.'

And he was wroth with this child. So departed Merlin; and came again in the likeness of an old man of four score years of age. Whereof the king was passing glad, for he seemed to be right wise. Then said the old man: 'Why are ye so sad?'

'I may well be sad,' said Arthur, 'for many things. A marvellous beast have I seen; and right now there was a child here and told me many things that meseemeth he should not know.'

'Yes , said the old man, 'the child told you truth, and more he would have told you an ye would have suffered him. And now leave this thy brooding and return unto the court. For this is the Questing Beast that thou hast seen, but the quest is not for thee. And he that follows it now is King Pellinore.'

'All that I may believe,' said the king, 'yet I list me not to return as yet, for the hunt is not yet ended.'

'This hunt hath never begun,' said Merlin, 'for thou camest not to hunt, but to seek Palomides, that thou art wroth withal. But him ye shall not find at this time.'

'What are ye,' said Arthur, 'that tell me this tidings?'

'Sir, I am Merlin, and I was in the child's likeness.'

'Ah,' said the king, 'ye are a wondrous man! But I marvel much that thou meddlest in this matter.'

'Marvel not,' said Merlin, 'and meddle not ye with Palomides, but return to the court.'

And as they talked, there came one with another horse for the king. And so the king mounted on his horse, and so rode unto Caerleon. And straightway Merlin by his arts was borne into another part of the forest, and there he found Palomides, that sat beneath a tree. And Merlin greeted Palomides, and he him again.[1]

'Who are ye,' said Merlin, 'that sit alone in the forest?'

'As for my name,' said Palomides, 'I list not to tell it thee, nor wouldst thou know it. For I am a knight of no name and no deeds, and so I will be rather than that others take order for my living.'

'Thou art Palomides', said Merlin, 'the son of Lord Esclabor and youngest of the knights of the Table Round. And how sayest thou that thou hast no name?'

'Who may ye be,' said Palomides, 'that know my name, yet erst,[2] methinks, I never saw thee.'

'I am Merlin, friend to King Arthur and to all the Round Table. And I would know what ye do here far from Caerleon and from the king.'

[1] in return. [2] before.

Then Palomides started up and looked upon Merlin, and Merlin was in his own shape again. And Palomides said:

'I am a knight made; and I would live as a knight, and not as a child that is ever told to do this and do that. For I was brought to Logres without my asking, and King Arthur made me of the company of the Round Table that had not deserved it, and so said the knights that were there. And now they would baptize me that I might be as all others are. And therefore I fled into this forest.'

'Well,' said Merlin, 'ye are a man, albeit young, and doubtless ye may be christened or not as ye will. And yet, now ye have made yourself free, ye do naught but sit idly beneath a tree.'

Then Palomides began to weep and said: 'In truth I know not what to do. Tell me what I must do, and I will obey you, sobeit I may do it alone.'

'Ye make conditions!' said Merlin, 'and hard is his way that would go it alone. But since ye have so chosen, I will tell you. Ye shall ride as a knight errant through this land till ye be come to Ireland, that was your mother's land. And when ye be come there, half of your lot shall encounter you. For your life shall be between a woman and a beast, and little joy shall ye have of one of them; and of the other I may not yet speak. But sithen[1] ye have chosen to take your life into your own keeping, thus it must be.'

And so Merlin vanished from before Palomides. And Palomides mounted upon his horse, and rode as adventure[2] took him. And so he rode many years, and did many great deeds; but ever he held him away from the wars of King Arthur and from tournaments, for he would live alone. And

[1] since.   [2] chance.

many damsels that he helped and rescued would have had his love, but he would none of them.

But on a day the Lady Lyones proclaimed a great joust at her castle, the Castle Perilous, and noise thereof came to Sir Palomides. Also he heard tell that his brethren Safere and Segwarides that were made knights after him, would be there. Then came Sir Palomides to the Castle Perilous and greeted his brethren, and much joy had they each of other.

And many great deeds did Sir Palomides at that tournament that all men marvelled. And scarce any knight might stand against him. But when the noise grew great upon him, then he remembered him of the words of Merlin, and suddenly he departed thence with no leave-taking. And so he rode until he came to the coast, and then took ship and came into Ireland.

III

The Fight in Ireland

AND when Sir Palomides was come to the court of King Anguish, that was King of Ireland, then was the king right glad of his coming, for the fame of his deeds was noised abroad, though ever he rode alone. And then at the court Sir Palomides saw the Princess Iseult that was the king's daughter, and him seemed that she was the fairest lady and maiden of the world. And Sir Palomides loved her passingly well, and proffered her many gifts. Yet for all his valour and his gifts she loved him not again. And the knights of Ireland marvelled much at La Beale Iseult for Sir Palomides was the mightiest knight in Ireland, and very goodly to look upon.

Now it chanced at that time that the king of Ireland had sent unto King Mark of Cornwall for to pay the truage[1] that was behind seven years. And he that bore the message was Sir Marhalt, the brother of the Queen of Ireland and knight of the Round Table. And King Mark was sore perplexed what to do, for no knight of Cornwall might withstand the might of Sir Marhalt, yet was he loth to pay the truage.

Then came King Mark's nephew, the young knight Sir Tristram of Lyones, son to King Meliodas, and said to his uncle that he would fight for the truage of Cornwall. And so he and Sir Marhalt fought upon an island by Tintagel. And

[1] tribute.

Sir Marhalt smote Sir Tristram a great wound in the side with his spear. And thereafter Sir Tristram smote Sir Marhalt so sore upon the helm that the sword cleft through the helm and a piece broke off thereof in Sir Marhalt's brain-pan. And then Sir Marhalt might no longer abide, but fled to his ships and so into Ireland. And none there might cure him, so that in a month he died. But the queen kept the piece of the sword that she found in his brain-pan.

And Sir Tristram returned unto Cornwall, and there was great rejoicing, and much honour did King Mark do unto him. But the wound in his side grew ever worse, and he was like to die. Then came a lady that was wise in medicine, and said to them that the spear that made the wound was envenomed; and never might Sir Tristram be whole but if that he went into the same country that the venom came from; and there might he be holpen, or else never.

So King Mark made ready a ship, and put therein Tristram upon a bed and with him Gouvernail his squire. And so they came into Ireland, into a harbour by a castle wherein were King Anguish and his queen. And as he lay upon his bed Sir Tristram harped a merry lay that the king knew not. And so he caused Sir Tristram to be brought before him in his bed as he lay. And then the king asked him what ailed him.

'I am of the country of Lyones,' said Tristram, 'and thus was I wounded in a battle that I fought for a lady's right.'

'So God me help,' said the king, 'ye shall have all the help in this land that ye may have here. Yet but late I lost the best knight in the world in Cornwall, and none here could save him.'

So Sir Tristram made semblance that he had been sorry, and that he knew not of this battle. And then he told the king that his name was Tramtrist, lest they knew who had slain Sir Marhalt.

Then the king for great favour made Tramtrist to be put in his daughter's ward and keeping, because she was a noble surgeon. And when she had searched him she found in the bottom of his wound that therein was poison; and so she healed him in a while. And therefore Sir Tramtrist cast great love to La Beale Iseult. And there Tramtrist learned her to harp, and she began to have a great fantasy[1] unto him.

And so oft times came Sir Palomides unto La Beale Iseult, for his love of her might not be let nor stayed.

All that espied Tramtrist and full well he knew Palomides for a noble knight and a mighty man. And wit you well, Sir Tramtrist had great despite at Palomides, for La Beale Iseult told Tramtrist that Palomides was in will to be christened for her sake. Thus was there great envy betwixt Tramtrist and Sir Palomides.

Then it befell that King Anguish let cry a great jousts and a great tournament for a Lady that was called the Lady of the Laundes, and she was nigh cousin unto the king. And what man won her, four days after should wed her and have all her lands. This cry was made in England, Wales and Scotland; and also in France and Brittany. So it befell upon a day La Beale Iseult came unto Tramtrist and told him of this tournament. He answered and said:

'Fair Lady, I am but a feeble knight; and of late I had been dead, had not your good ladyship been. Now, fair lady, what would ye that I should do in this matter? Well ye wot, my lady, that I may not joust.'

'Ah Tramtrist,' said La Beale Iseult, 'why will ye not have

[1] love.

1 The Queen gripped the sword and ran upon
    Tristram in his bath (*see page* 32)

2 Sir Palomides and Sir Safere departed, and with them
    rode Igraine the Fair (*see page* 100)

ado at that tournament? For well I wot that Sir Palomides will be there, and to do what he may. And therefore, Sir Tramtrist, I pray you for to be there; or else Sir Palomides is like to win the degree.'

'Madam, as for that, it may be so for he is a proved knight; and I am but a young knight and late made. And the first battle that ever I did, it mishapped me to be sore wounded, as ye see. But, an I wist that ye would be my better lady, at that tournament will I be on this covenant: so that ye will keep my counsel, and let no creature have knowledge that I shall joust but yourself and such as ye will to keep your counsel, my poor person shall I jeopard thus for your sake, that peradventure Sir Palomides shall know when that I am come.'

Thereto said La Beale Iseult: 'Do your best: and, as I can, I shall purvey horse and armour for you at my device.'

'As ye will, so be it,' said Sir Tramtrist. 'I will be at your commandment.'

So at the day of jousts there came Sir Palomides with a black shield; and he overthrew many knights, that all people had marvel. For he put to the worse Sir Gawaine, Sir Gaheris, Sir Agravaine, King Bagdemagus, Sir Kay, Sir Dodinas le Savage, Sir Sagramore le Desirous, Sir Gumret le Petit and Sir Griflet le Fise de Dieu. All these the first day Sir Palomides struck down to earth. And then all knights were adread of Sir Palomides; and many called him the knight with the black shield. So that day Sir Palomides had great worship.[1]

Now it chanced that there came a certain squire that knew Sir Tristram aforetime; and when he espied him he fell flat to his feet. And therewithal Sir Tristram lifted him up quickly,

[1] honour.

B

and prayed him heartily in no wise to tell his name. And that espied La Beale Iseult what courtesy the squire made to Tristram. Then had she great suspicion that he was some man of worship proved; and therewith she comforted herself and cast more love unto him.

And so on the morn Sir Palomides made him ready to come into the field, as he did the first day; and there he smote down the King with the Hundred Knights and the King of Scots. Now La Beale Iseult had ordained and well arrayed Sir Tristram with white horse and white armour; and right so she let put him out at a privy postern. And he came so into the field as it had been a bright angel. And anon Sir Palomides espied him; and then he feutred[1] his spear unto Sir Tristram, and he again unto him; and there Sir Tristram smote down Sir Palomides unto the earth.

And then was there great noise of people; some said Sir Palomides had a fall; some said the knight with the black shield had a fall. And wit you well La Beale Iseult was passing glad. And then Sir Gawaine and his fellows nine had marvel who it might be that had smitten down Sir Palomides. Then would there none joust with Sir Tristram; but all that were there forsook him, most and least.

Now when Sir Palomides received his fall, wit ye well that he was sore ashamed, and as privily as he might he withdrew him out of the field. All that espied Sir Tristram and lightly[2] he rode after Sir Palomides and bade him turn; for better he would assay him or ever be departed. Then Sir Palomides turned him and either lashed at other with swords: but at the first stroke Sir Tristram smote down Sir Palomides and gave him such a stroke upon the head that he fell to the earth.

[1] fixed (his spear) in its rest.   [2] quickly

So then Sir Tristram bade him yield him and do his commandment or else he would slay him. When Sir Palomides beheld his countenance, he dread his buffets so that he granted all his askings.

'Well,' said Sir Tristram, 'this shall be your charge. First, upon pain of your life, that ye forsake my lady, La Beale Iseult, and in no manner of wise that ye draw no more to her. Also, this twelve month and a day that ye bear none arms neither none harness of war. Now promise me this, or here shalt thou die.'

'Alas,' said Sir Palomides, 'for ever am I shamed!'

Then he swore as Sir Tristram had commanded him. So for despite and anger Sir Palomides cut off his harness and threw them away. And Sir Tristram rode privily unto the pasture where La Beale Iseult awaited him; and there she made him great cheer and thanked God of his good speed.[1]

So upon a day the queen and Iseult made a bath for Sir Tristram. And when he was in his bath, they roamed up and down in the chamber the while Gouvernail attended upon Tristram. The queen beheld his sword as it lay upon his bed; and then by ill fortune she drew the sword out of its scabbard, and then she saw that within a foot and a half of the point there was a great piece thereof outbroken off the edge. And then she remembered her of a piece of a sword that was found in the brain-pan of Sir Marhalt that was her brother.

'Alas,' then said she unto her daughter, 'this is the same traitor knight that slew my brother, thine uncle.'

When Iseult heard her say so she was sore abashed, for passing well she loved Tristram, and full well she knew the cruelness of her mother the queen.

[1] achievement.

So anon therewithal the queen went unto her own chamber and sought her coffer, and there she took out the piece of the sword, that was pulled out of Sir Marhalt's brain-pan after that he was dead. And then she ran with the piece of iron unto the sword; and when she put that piece of steel and iron unto the sword, it was as meet as it might be when it was new broken.

And then the queen gripped that sword in her hand fiercely and with all her might she ran straight upon Tristram where he sat in his bath. And there she had riven him through had not Gouvernail been. He gat her in his arms, and pulled the sword from her; and else she had thrust him through. So when she was thus let,[1] she ran unto the king her husband, and told him all.

And then the king went unto the chamber where Sir Tristram was, and asked him who he was and wherefore he had slain Sir Marhalt. So Sir Tristram told him his name and all the tale of the fight for the truage of Cornwall.

And then the king found Sir Tristram not greatly to blame, yet could he not thereafter stay at that court. So the king made him to take his leave without hurt or let of any man, and so Sir Tristram departed out of Ireland, and came unto Cornwall unto his uncle King Mark.

Now it chanced that Sir Segwarides had come into Cornwall, seeking his brother, Sir Palomides. And King Mark showed him much favour and made him to wed an Earl's daughter that hight the lady Iverna. Yet King Mark did not honestly, for he loved that lady himself and had had ado with her. And she was deemed the fairest lady in all Cornwall.

And so after Sir Tristram was come it chanced on a day

[1] prevented.

that he beheld the Lady Iverna and set great love upon her, and she loved him again. Then King Mark understood that, and was jealous; for he loved her passingly well.

IV

Sir Tristram and the Lady Iverna

So it befell upon a day that this lady sent a dwarf unto Sir Tristram, and bade him, as he loved her, that he would be with her the next night following. Also she charged him that he come not to her but if he be well armed; for her lord was called a good knight. Sir Tristram answered to the dwarf that he would not fail, and therewith the dwarf departed.

Now King Mark espied that the dwarf was with Sir Tristram upon message from Segwarides' wife. Then King Mark sent for the dwarf, and when he was come he made the dwarf by force to tell him all why and wherefore that he came on message to Sir Tristram.

'Well,' said King Mark, 'go where thou wilt, but upon pain of death that thou say no word that thou spake with me.'

So the dwarf departed from the king. And that same night that the steven[1] was set betwixt Segwarides' wife and Sir Tristram, so King Mark armed and made him ready and took two knights of his council with him. And so he rode before for to abide by the ways for to wait upon Sir Tristram.

And as Sir Tristram came riding upon his way with his spear in his hands, King Mark came hurtling upon him and his two knights suddenly; and all three smote him with their spears, and King Mark hurt Sir Tristram upon the breast

[1] assignation.

right sore. And then Sir Tristram feutred his spear and smote King Mark so sore that he rushed him to the earth and bruised him that he lay still in a swoon; and long it was or[1] he might stir himself. And then he ran to the one knight and after to the other, and smote them to the earth that they lay still.

And therewithal Sir Tristram rode forth to the lady, and found her abiding him at a postern. And then she welcomed him fair, and either clypped[2] other in arms. And so she let put up his horse in the best wise, and then she unarmed him, and so they supped lightly and went to bed with great joy and pleasance. And so in his raging[3] he took no keep of his green[4] wound that King Mark had given him; and so Sir Tristram bled both the oversheet and the undersheet and the pillows and the head sheet.

And within a while there came one that warned that fair lady that her lord, Sir Segwarides, was near at hand within a bow draught.[5] So she made Sir Tristram to arise; and so he armed him and took his horse and so departed. So by then was Sir Segwarides come; and when he found his bed troubled and broken, he went near and looked by candle-light and saw that there had lain a wounded knight.

'Ah false harlot,' he said, 'why hast thou betrayed me?' And therewithal he swang out a sword, and said: 'But if thou tell me who hath been here, now shalt thou die!'

'Ah my lord, mercy!' said the lady, and held up her hands: 'Slay me not, and I shall tell you who hath been here. Here was Sir Tristram with me; and by the way, as he came to me-ward, he was sore wounded.'

'Ah false harlot, where is he become?'

[1] before. [2] embraced. [3] passion. [4] fresh. [5] bow shot.

'Sir', she said, 'he is armed and departed on horseback, not yet hence half a mile.'

Then Sir Segwarides armed him lightly and gat his horse and rode after Sir Tristram the straight way unto Tintagel; and within a while he overtook Sir Tristram, and bade him turn. And therewithal Segwarides smote Sir Tristram with a spear that it all to-brast;[1] and then he swang out his sword, and smote fast at Sir Tristram.

'Sir knight,' said Sir Tristram, 'I counsel you that ye smite no more. Howbeit for the wrong I have done you I will forbear you as long as I may.'

'Nay,' said Sir Segwarides, 'that shall not be. For either thou shalt die or else I.'

Then Sir Tristram drew out his sword and hurtled his horse unto him freshly, and through the waist of the body he smote Sir Segwarides, that he fell to the earth in swoon.

And so Sir Tristram departed and left him there, and rode unto Tintagel and took his lodging secretly, for he would not it be known that he was hurt. And Sir Segwarides' men rode after their master and brought him home on his shield. And there he lay long ere he was whole, but at the last he recovered.

Also King Mark would not be a-known of[2] that he had done unto Sir Tristram when they met that night; and as for Sir Tristram, he knew not that King Mark had met with him. And so the king came askance to Sir Tristram to comfort him as he lay sick in his bed. But as long as King Mark lived he loved never after Sir Tristram. So after that, though there were fair speech, love was there none.

And thus it passed on many weeks and days, and all was forgiven and forgotten. For Sir Segwarides durst not have ado

---

[1] broke in pieces. [2] did not wish to disclose.

with Sir Tristram because of his noble prowess, and also because he was nephew unto King Mark. Therefore he let it overslip; for he that hath a privy hurt is loth to have a shame outward.

Then it befell upon a day that the good knight, Sir Bleoberis de Ganis, brother unto Sir Blamore de Ganis, a nigh cousin unto the good knight Sir Lancelot du Lake, came unto the court of King Mark. And there he asked King Mark to give him a boon, what gift soever he would ask. When the king heard him ask so, he marvelled of his asking: but, because he was a knight of the Round Table and of great renown, King Mark granted him his whole asking.

Then said Sir Bleoberis: 'I will have the fairest lady in your court that me list to choose.'

'I may not say thee nay,' said King Mark: 'Now choose her at thy adventure.'

And so Sir Bleoberis did choose Sir Segwarides' wife, and took her by the hand, and so he went his way with her. And so he took his horse, and made set her behind his squire, and rode upon his way.

When Sir Segwarides heard tell that his lady was gone with a knight of King Arthur's court, then he armed him and rode after that knight to rescue his lady. And when Sir Bleoberis was gone with the lady, King Mark and all the court were wroth that she was had away. And there were certain ladies that knew that there was great love between Sir Tristram and her, and that the lady loved Sir Tristram above all other knights. Then was there one of those ladies that rebuked Sir Tristram in the horriblest wise, and called him coward knight that he would for shame of his knighthood to see a lady so shamefully taken away from his uncle's court. But she meant

that either of them loved other with entire heart. But Sir
Tristram answered her thus:

'Fair lady, it is not my part to have ado in such matters while
her lord and husband is present here. And if so be that her lord
had not been here in this court, then for the worship of this
court peradventure I would have been the champion. And if
so be Sir Segwarides speed not well, it may happen that I will
speak with that good knight, or he pass far from this country.'

Then within a while came Sir Segwarides' squire and told
in the court that his master was beaten sore and wounded
to the point of death. As he would have rescued his lady, Sir
Bleoberis overturned him and sore wounded him. Then was
King Mark heavy thereof and all the court. And when Sir
Tristram heard of this, he was ashamed and aggrieved. And
anon he armed him and rode on horseback; and Gouvernail,
his servant, bore his shield and his spear.

So Sir Tristram departed and rode onward on his way.
And then was he ware before him in a valley where rode Sir
Bleoberis with Sir Segwarides' lady that rode behind his
squire upon a palfrey. Then Sir Tristram rode more than a
pace until that he had overtaken him. Then spake Sir
Tristram: 'Abide, knight of Arthur's court! Bring again that
lady or deliver her to me!'

'I will do neither one nor other,' said Sir Bleoberis, 'for I
dread no Cornish knight so sore that me list to deliver her.'

'Why,' said Sir Tristram, 'may not a Cornish knight do as
well as another knight? So now defend you!'

So they departed and came together like thunder, and
either bore other down, horse and man, to the earth. Then
they avoided[1] their horses, and lashed together eagerly with

[1] dismounted from.

swords and mightily, now here now there, tracing and traversing[1] on the right hand and on the left hand more than two hours. And sometimes they rushed together with such a might that they both lay grovelling on the earth. Then Sir Bleoberis started aback and said thus: 'Now, gentle knight, awhile hold your hand and let us speak together.'

'Say on what ye will,' said Sir Tristram, 'and I will answer you as I can.'

'Sir,' said Sir Bleoberis, 'I would wit of whence ye were and of whom ye be come and what is your name.'

'So God me help,' said Sir Tristram, 'I fear not to tell you my name. Wit you well I am King Meliodas' son, and my mother is King Mark's sister, and my name is Sir Tristram de Lyones, and King Mark is mine uncle.'

'Truly,' said Sir Bleoberis, 'I am right glad of you: for ye are he that slew Sir Marhalt hand for hand on an island for the truage of Cornwall. Also ye overcame Sir Palomides the good knight, at the tournament in Ireland where he beat Sir Gawaine and his nine fellows.'

'So God me help,' said Sir Tristram, 'wit you well I am the same knight. Now I have told you my name, tell me yours.'

'With good will. My name is Sir Bleoberis de Ganis, and my brother hight Sir Blamore de Ganis, and we be sister's children unto my lord Sir Lancelot du Lake, that we call one of the best knights of the world.'

'That is truth,' said Sir Tristram, 'Sir Lancelot is called peerless of courtesy and of knighthood; and for his sake I will not with my good will fight any more with you for the great love I have to Sir Lancelot.'

'In good faith,' said Sir Bleoberis, 'as for me, I would be

[1] checking and dodging.

loth to fight with you; but sithen ye follow me here to have this lady, I shall proffer you kindness and courtesy right here upon this ground. This lady shall be set betwixt us both; and who that she will go unto of you and me, let him have her in peace.'

'I will well,' said Sir Tristram, 'for as I deem, she will leave you and come to me.'

'That ye shall prove anon,' said Sir Bleoberis.

So when she was set betwixt them, she said these words unto Sir Tristram:

'Wit thou well, Sir Tristram de Lyones, that but late thou wast the man in the world that I most loved and trusted, and I weened ye had loved me above all ladies again. But when thou sawest this knight lead me away, thou madest no shift to rescue me, but sufferedst my lord, Sir Segwarides, to ride after me. But until that time I weened ye had loved me. And therefore now I forsake thee, never to love thee more.'

And therewithal she went unto Sir Bleoberis. When Sir Tristram saw her do so, he was wonderly wroth with that lady and ashamed to go to the court. Then said Sir Bleoberis:

'Ye are in the blame, for I hear by this lady's words that she trusted you above all earthly knights, and, as she saith, ye have deceived her. Therefore wit ye well there may no man hold that that will away and, rather than ye should be heartily displeased with me, I would ye had her and she would abide with you.'

'Nay,' said the lady, 'I will never go with him: for he that I loved and weened that he had loved me forsook me at my need. Therefore, Sir Tristram, ride as thou camest. For though thou hadst overcome this knight, as thou wert likely, with thee never would I have gone. And I shall pray this knight so fair of his knighthood that or ever he pass this country he will lead me to the abbey where my lord, Sir Segwarides, lies.'

'So God me help,' said Sir Bleoberis, 'I let you wit this, good knight Sir Tristram: because King Mark gave me a choice of a gift in his court and so this lady liked[1] me best—notwithstanding she is wedded and hath a lord—and I have also fulfilled my quest, she shall be sent unto her husband again; and especial most for your sake, Sir Tristram. An she would go with you, I would ye had her.'

'I thank you,' said Sir Tristram, 'but for her sake I shall beware what manner of lady I shall love or trust. For had her lord, Sir Segwarides, been away from the court, I should have been the first that followed you. But since she hath refused me, I shall know her passingly well on whom I deem to set my love or trust.'

And so they took their leave and departed. And Sir Tristram rode unto Tintagel; and Sir Bleoberis rode unto the abbey where Sir Segwarides lay sore wounded, and there he delivered his lady and departed as a noble knight. So when Sir Segwarides saw his lady he was greatly comforted: and then she told him that Sir Tristram had done great battle with Sir Bleoberis and caused him to bring her again. And that false word pleased Sir Segwarides greatly, that Sir Tristram would do so much. Also that lady told all the battle unto King Mark betwixt Sir Tristram and Sir Bleoberis.

[1] pleased.

V

The Fight in Cornwall

AND thereafter King Mark for very jealousy cast all the
ways that he might to destroy Sir Tristram. And at
the last he thought to send him into Ireland for La
Beale Iseult, for Sir Tristram had so praised her for her beauty
and goodness that King Mark said he would wed her. Also he
deemed that the queen of Ireland would find means to slay
Sir Tristram for Sir Marhalt's sake.

But when Sir Tristram was come into Ireland King Anguish
made him good cheer and would not suffer the queen to come
nigh him. And full soon he was accorded with him for his
daughter; and so Sir Tristram and La Beale Iseult took ship
to sail unto Cornwall. And Sir Tristram turned again unto La
Beale Iseult, for in the love of the lady Iverna he had somewhat
forgot her.

Now it chanced that the queen had given unto Dame
Brangwain, that was chief gentlewoman unto Iseult, a little
flask of gold wherein was a strong potion. And the queen
charged Brangwain to give it unto King Mark and Iseult on
the day they should wed, for then either should love other all
the days of their life. And Sir Tristram and La Beale Iseult
found that flask in the cabin when they were athirst, and so
they drank it. And thereafter the love betwixt Sir Tristram
and La Beale Iseult never departed all the days of their life.

Then they came unto Cornwall and Sir Tristram delivered

La Beale Iseult unto King Mark, and the King was right glad of her. Yet ever with Dame Brangwain's aid did she deceive the King that never did he have ado with her.

And so they made a great feast for the wedding and many came to the feast. And at that time Sir Palomides was come into Cornwall, and abode secretly with his brother, Sir Segwarides. For when that he departed out of Ireland Sir Palomides went into England and abode in the forests. And he sought no adventure till the time of his oath was ended. And ever day and night he thought upon La Beale Iseult.

And so, when the time was come, he took his armour again, and he thought to go unto Ireland. But when he heard tidings that Sir Tristram and La Beale Iseult had sailed to Cornwall, then he also went into Cornwall. But when he saw that King Mark would wed La Beale Iseult, then he kept himself close hid till he saw how it would be.

Now after that King Mark had wedded La Beale Iseult and the feast was done, two ladies that longed[1] unto the Queen of Ireland ordained for hate and envy for to destroy Dame Brangwain, that was maiden and lady unto La Beale Iseult. And she was sent into the forest for to fetch herbs, and there was she met and bound hand and foot to a tree and so was she bounden three days. And by fortune Sir Palomides found Dame Brangwain, and there he delivered her from death, and brought her to a nunnery there beside for to be recovered.

When Iseult the queen missed her maiden, wit you well she was right heavy as ever any queen might be; for of all earthly women she loved her best and most, cause why she came with her out of her country. And so upon a day Queen Iseult walked into the forest to put away her thoughts, and there

[1] belonged.

she went unto a well and made great moan for this maiden.

And suddenly there came Sir Palomides unto her and heard all her complaint. Then said Sir Palomides: 'Madam Iseult, an ye would grant me my boon, I shall bring again to you Dame Brangwain safe and sound.'

Then the queen was so glad of his proffer that suddenly unavised[1] she granted all his asking.

'Well, Madam,' said Sir Palomides, 'I trust to your promise; and, if ye will abide half an hour here, I shall bring her to you.'

Then Sir Palomides rode forth his way to that nunnery, and lightly he came again with Dame Brangwain: but by her good will she would not have come to the queen, for cause she stood in fear of her life. Notwithstanding, half against her will, she came with Sir Palomides unto the queen. And when the queen saw her she was passing glad.

'Now, Madam,' said Sir Palomides, 'remember upon your promise, for I have fulfilled my promise.'

'Sir Palomides,' said the queen, 'I wot not what is your desire. But I will that ye wit, howbeit that I proffered you largely, I thought none evil; neither, I warn you, none evil will I do.'

'Madam,' said Sir Palomides, 'as at this time ye shall not know my desire. But before my lord, your husband, there shall I have my desire that ye have promised me.'

And then the queen rode home unto the king, and Sir Palomides rode with her. And when Sir Palomides came before the king, he said:

'Sir King, I require thee, as thou art righteous king, that ye judge me the right. I promised your queen, my lady Dame Iseult, to bring again Dame Brangwain that she had lost, upon

[1] unwarily.

covenant that she should grant me a boon that I should ask. And without grudging or advisement[1] she granted me.'

'What say ye, my lady?' said the king.

'It is as he saith, so God me help! To say the sooth, I promised him his asking for the love and joy I had to see her.'

'Well, Madam,' said the King, 'even if ye were hasty to grant what boon he would ask, I would well that ye performed your promise.'

Then said Sir Palomides: 'I will have your queen, to lead her and to govern her whereas me list.'

Therewith the king stood still and bethought him of Sir Tristram, and deemed that he would rescue her. So then the king answered and said: 'Take her to thee, and the adventures withal that will fall of it: for, as I suppose, thou wilt not enjoy her no while.'

Then said the queen: 'Wit thou well I fear not greatly to go with thee, howbeit thou hast me at advantage upon my promise; for I doubt not I shall be worshipfully rescued from thee.'

'As for that,' said Sir Palomides, 'I dare right well abide the adventure.'

So Queen Iseult was set behind Sir Palomides, and they rode their way. And anon the king sent unto Sir Tristram, but in no wise he could not be found, for he was in the forest a-hunting. For that was always his custom, but if he used arms, to chase and to hunt in the forest.

'Alas,' said the king, 'now am I shamed for ever that by mine own assent my lady and my queen should be devoured.'

Yet offered not one of those Cornish knights for to go and joust with Palomides for the queen. So then came there forth a knight that hight Lambegus, and said:

[1] reflexion.

'My Lord, sith that Sir Tristram may not be found and all these are coward knights, I, wounded though I be, will ride after your queen and rescue you, or else I will be beaten.'

'Gramercy,' said the king, 'as I live, Sir Lambegus, I shall deserve it.'

Now this knight, Sir Lambegus, had been tutor to Sir Bors de Ganis in the court of his father, King Bors. And he had given himself prisoner to King Claudas, that warred against Ganis, for to save the city of Ganis. And for his noblesse King Claudas set him at liberty. And thither he had come into Cornwall, where he had encountered two knights that had wounded him; and so was he at the court to be healed of his wounds. So Sir Lambegus armed him and rode after Sir Palomides so fast as he might, and then within a while he overtook them. And then Sir Palomides left the queen, and said: 'What art thou? Art thou Sir Tristram?'

'Nay,' he said, 'my name is Sir Lambegus.'

'That me regrets,' said Sir Palomides, 'I had liever thou hadst been Sir Tristram.'

'I believe you well,' said Sir Lambegus, 'but when thou meetest with Sir Tristram, thou shalt have both thy hands full.'

And then they hurtled together and all to-brast their spears; and then they pulled out their swords and hewed on their helms and hauberks. And at the last Sir Palomides gave Sir Lambegus such a wound that he fell down like a dead man to the earth. Then he looked after La Beale Iseult, and she was gone he wist not where. Wit you well that Sir Palomides was never so heavy!

So the queen ran into the forest to a brook hight Ornise that traversed the forest of Morois; for she thought to drown herself. And, as good fortune would, there came a knight of

Cornwall to her that had a castle there beside, and his name was Sir Adherp. And when he found the queen in that mischief, he rescued her and brought her to his castle. And when he wist what she was, he armed him and took his horse, and said he would be avenged on Sir Palomides.

And so he rode unto the time he met him, and there Sir Palomides wounded him sore. And by force he made him to tell the cause why he did battle with him, and he told him how he led the queen Iseult unto his own castle.

Sir Palomides rode till he came to the castle. And at a window Queen Iseult saw Sir Palomides; and then she made the gates to be shut strongly. And when he saw he might not enter into the castle, he put off his horse bridle and his saddle and so put his horse to pasture, and set himself down at the gate like a man that was out of his wit, that recked not of himself.

Now turn we unto Sir Tristram, that, when he was come home and wist that La Beale Iseult was gone with Sir Palomides, wit you well he was wroth out of measure.

'Alas,' said Sir Tristram, 'I am this day shamed.'

Then he called Gouvernail, his man, and said: 'Haste thee, that I were armed and on horseback. For well I wot Sir Lambegus hath no might nor strength to withstand Sir Palomides. Alas I had not been in his stead!'

So anon he was armed and horsed and rode after into the forest; and within a while he found Sir Lambegus nigh unto death wounded. And Sir Tristram bore him to a forester and charged him to keep him well. And then he rode forth and found Sir Adherp sore wounded. And he told all, and how the queen had drowned herself, had not he been, and how for her sake he took upon him to do battle with Sir Palomides.

'Gramercy,' said Sir Tristram, 'of thy great goodness.'

And so Sir Tristram and Gouvernail rode till they came to the castle and there at the gate sat Sir Palomides as he had been asleep, and his horse pastured afore him.

'Now go thou, Gouvernail,' said Sir Tristram, 'and bid him awake and make him ready.'

So Gouvernail rode unto him and said:

'Sir Palomides, arise, and take to thine harness!' But he was in such a study he heard not what he said. So Gouvernail came again to Sir Tristram, and told him he slept or else he was mad.

'Go thou again,' said Sir Tristram, 'and tell him I am here, his mortal foe.'

So Gouvernail rode again, and put upon him the butt of his spear, and said: 'Sir Palomides, make thee ready! For wit thou well Sir Tristram hoveth yonder, and sendeth thee word he is thy mortal foe.'

And therewithal Sir Palomides arose stiffly without any words, and gat his horse anon and saddled him and bridled him, and lightly he leapt upon him, and gat his spear in his hand. And either feutred their spears and hurtled fast together, and anon Sir Tristram smote down Sir Palomides over his horse's tail. Then lightly Sir Palomides put his shield before him and drew his sword.

And there began strong battle on both parts, for both they fought for the love of one lady. And she lay on the walls and beheld them how they fought out of measure. And either were wounded passing sore, but Sir Palomides was much sorer wounded. And they fought thus, tracing and traversing more than two hours, that Queen Iseult well nigh swooned for dole and sorrow. And she said:

'Alas that one I loved, and yet do, and the other I love not, that they should fight! And yet it were great pity that I should see Sir Palomides slain (for well I know, by that the end be done, Sir Palomides is but a dead man) because that he is not christened; and I would be loth that he should die a saracen.'

And therewithal she came down, and besought them for her love to fight no more.

'Ah Madam,' said Sir Tristram, 'what mean ye? Will ye have me shamed? For well ye know that I will be ruled by you.'

'Ah mine own lord,' said La Beale Iseult, 'full well ye wot I would not your dishonour! But I would that ye would for my sake spare this unhappy saracen, Sir Palomides.'

'Madam,' said Sir Tristram, 'I will leave for your sake.'

Then said she to Sir Palomides: 'This shall be thy charge. Thou shalt go out of this country while I am therein.'

'Madam, I will obey your commandment,' said Sir Palomides, 'which is sore against my will.'

'Then take thy way,' said Queen Iseult, 'unto the court of King Arthur, and there recommend me unto Queen Guinevere, and tell her that I send her word that there be within this land but four lovers, and they are Sir Lancelot and Dame Guinevere, and Sir Tristram and Queen Iseult. And as for thee, come thou never nigh me save that I be come into Logres.'

And so Sir Palomides departed with great heaviness. And Sir Tristram besought Queen Iseult that she would go with him into the realm of Logres, but at that time she would not. So Sir Tristram brought the queen again unto King Mark, and then there was made great joy of their home-coming.

VI

Sir Palomides Takes the Quest

Now, as Sir Palomides journeyed into Logres he came to a great forest. And sithen he took no thought for his way, ere long he was lost in that forest. And he found neither hut nor castle whereat he might rest; and being weary he sat him down beneath a great tree.

And as he sat there anon there came an old man to him that asked him what he did.

'Old Sir,' said Sir Palomides, 'I do naught, for naught is there to do in this forest.'

'That is ill spoken,' said the old man, 'for much adventure there is in this forest, and it is not meet for a knight errant to sit idly and dream of a lady that is not for him.'

Then Sir Palomides started up and said: 'How know ye my dreams?'

But ere the old man could answer, there was a sound of a great baying of hounds and Sir Palomides looked to see the hounds and the hunt that would come. But instead came a beast, the strangest that ever he saw: for it had a serpent's head and a body like a leopard; it was buttocked like a lion and footed like a hart. And in the beast's belly was ever the noise of the hounds that Sir Palomides heard.

And the beast looked once upon Sir Palomides and upon the old man, and so it passed on its way.

'There is thy quest,' said the old man, 'and that thou mayest attain, if thou wilt, but Iseult never.'

'Who art thou,' said Sir Palomides, 'that knowest what I may do and what I may not do? And how knowest thou me that am but a young knight?'

'I am Merlin,' said the old man, 'a friend to thy mother, Etain, and to thee. And would that ye had never met with this Iseult, for nought but grief will ye have of her. For a mighty knight shall ye be; and a mightier yet might be if ye would but hold to one purpose and carry a quest through to the end. So now is this quest of the beast given you; and it was aforetimes the quest of King Pellinore that hath now been foully slain by Sir Gawaine and his brethren; yet he never attained it.'

And then Merlin told Sir Palomides all the story of the beast, so that Sir Palomides marvelled.

And Merlin said: 'See that you follow this beast with a single mind, as did not King Pellinore. For the Beast is the quest for him that can endure all things unto the end and is not led astray by anger or despair or hope of renown.'

'I will take the quest,' said Sir Palomides, 'and follow the Questing Beast. But I pray thee tell me, when I attain the beast, must I slay it or take it captive? And what is the end thereof?'

But he found no answer as at that time, for Merlin had departed from him secretly. So Sir Palomides took his horse and rode after the beast, but nowise could he find it nor hear its noise.

And so he rode more than a year, and on a day he met with a knight that proffered him to joust.

'I will not joust,' said Sir Palomides, 'for I follow the Questing Beast, and am not at leisure for other play.'

'Nay, but ye shall joust,' said that knight, 'for I am Sir

Lamorak de Galis, and that beast was my father's quest when he was on live, and by right the quest is mine. And never shall ye have it but that ye vanquish me in fair fight.'

So then they feutred their spears and came hurtling together, and Sir Palomides smote Sir Lamorak over his horse's crop, and so passed on his way. And with that came Sir Tristram, that had been sent out of Cornwall by La Beale Iseult for fear of King Mark. And he too proffered Sir Palomides to joust and Sir Palomides served him as he had served Sir Lamorak. Yet Sir Palomides knew not Sir Tristram for he was disguised.

And Sir Tristram was so wroth at his overthrow that what with wrath and with longing for Iseult he was nigh out of his wits. And by chance he lodged that night at a castle where was Sir Segwarides and his wife, the Lady Iverna, that erst Sir Tristram had loved. And when they saw him so wan and distressed and his armour all dirtied, they asked him his name and what had befallen him. And Sir Tristram told how he had had the worse in a joust with Sir Palomides, but his name he would not tell. And when Sir Segwarides heard tell that his brother, Sir Palomides, was in those parts, he started up and took his horse, and rode forth to seek him.

But the Lady Iverna had a deeming who this knight might be. And when she deemed that he was unarmed and sleeping, she took a candle and went softly to his room, and saw that it was Tristram.

And then she put out the candle and hid her behind the curtains of the room; and then she began to rail upon Sir Tristram and to mock him in a loud voice, and said:

'Fie on thee, Sir Tristram, that hast lost thy name and thy prowess! For now King Mark enjoys thy lady, and the meanest knight errant may make thee bite the dust. Verily a by-word and a mockery art thou become among knights!'

And Sir Tristram awoke, and when he heard her words and saw no one, a madness came upon him. And he gave a loud cry, and ran out of the house naked as he was. And upon the next day it chanced that Sir Palomides came to the castle and lodged there. And he greeted the Lady Iverna, but made no converse with her. So then she began to speak softly, as though to herself, and said how strange a thing it was that Sir Tristram was not in Cornwall, but was gone no man knew where. And then she spake of the Lady Iseult that was left alone in Cornwall, and of her beauty and her loneliness.

So at the last Sir Palomides heard her words, and bethought him of his love for Queen Iseult, and forgot his quest. And he spoke long with the Lady Iverna, and early on the morrow he took his horse and rode towards Cornwall.

And anon the Lady Iverna called unto her a servant and bade him ride with all speed unto King Mark with a message. And the message said that Sir Tristram had run mad in the forest, and that in his madness he had sworn to kill King Mark wheresoever he might find him. And it chanced that the servant found King Mark that had gone hunting in the forest of Morois, and the King was alone for he had lost his people that were with him. So the servant gave his message to the King, and so departed.

And King Mark was sore afraid, and began to make his way out of the forest as fast as he might. And as he passed by an empty house he saw afar off a knight approaching. And he deemed that it might be Sir Tristram. And so he hid himself in the house between two walls.

And thereafter came the knight to the house. And the

knight was Sir Segwarides, that was sore weary with searching for Sir Palomides. And Sir Segwarides entered into a room of the house and laid him down to rest.

And soon thereafter, when it was dark, Sir Palomides came to the house. And he deemed that it was empty, and sat him down therein, and began to make a doleful lay, and said:

'Alas, this Love! For love at first is like the fair dawn of day that maketh the birds to sing and amorous knights to hurtle hither and thither. But suddenly the weather changeth: the storm comes, and out goes happiness. He who trusts in love is like the fool that climbs a mountain to seize the moon he seeth resting upon its peak. Love for the lover is like a candle in the darkness of the night. Its glow makes light for all save him who bears it. Yet, as the loveliest of flowers is born upon a thorn bush, so out of cruel love comes courtesy, which is man's highest grace.'

With that Sir Segwarides awoke, and great joy had he to find his brother. And as they spoke together they heard a great coughing, and Sir Segwarides went forth to see what this might be. Anon he found King Mark, that essayed to steal away secretly but was betrayed by his cough. Now King Mark was ashamed that he had been found so hiding, and made as though he were but a simple knight. But Sir Segwarides knew him and called him by name.

'What doth so great a king alone in such a house as this?' said Sir Palomides. 'Peradventure ye seek Sir Tristram, that they say is run mad in this forest.'

'In truth,' said King Mark, 'I seek not Sir Tristram. But, an he is truly mad, I fear he may do me some injury.'

'That might he well do,' said Sir Palomides, 'an he were in

his right mind. And should he meet you and pass you by, that would be very proof of his madness.'

'As for that,' said King Mark, 'ye may say as ye will. Yet I pray you go with me till we be come forth of this forest, for greatly I fear me of Sir Tristram.'

So they were agreed, and rode forth together. And as they came forth of the forest they met with Sir Lancelot, who greeted them fair and they him again. And Sir Lancelot told them of a great tournament that should be held that day sennight at the Castle of Maidens. Also he told them that Sir Tristram had been found of Sir Dinadan as he ran mad in the forest; and Sir Dinadan had taken him to a wise woman that was mother to the good knight Sir Persides. And now was Sir Tristram cured of his madness.

And as they spoke together there came a messenger seeking Sir Palomides, and told him that his mother, the Lady Etain, sought him high and low throughout the land. And now she abode him in a castle not far from that place. So Sir Palomides went with the messenger, and the other knights departed from him.

And when Sir Palomides was come unto his mother's castle, wit you well that the Lady Etain was right glad to see him, and greeted him full lovingly.

'My dear son,' said she, 'long have I sought you. For I know that ye have left this quest that Merlin gave you, and that ye will, certes, go to this tournament. But yet Merlin told you not all that ye must do. And therefore I pray you that ye hearken to me and that ye be christened. For no knight may triumph in his own power in a quest or in a tournament save with the aid of our Lord Jesus Christ.'

'Nay,' said Sir Palomides, 'I will not be christened as at this time. For, though I believe, I would not have it said of me that I became a Christian but to win worship. And when I have proved my might upon Christian knights, then will I be christened.'

And at that his mother wept, but by no means could she persuade him. And when Sir Palomides had stayed three days in that place, he took leave of the Lady Etain, and so departed to the tournament.

VII

The Castle of Maidens

Now turn we unto Sir Tristram that was cured of his madness, and rode at adventure and Sir Dinadan and Sir Persides with him. And when Sir Tristram heard of the tournament at the Castle of Maidens, he said he would go thither. And Sir Persides also said he would go with him, but first he must return to his own castle. So Persides departed and Sir Tristram and Sir Dinadan rode on their way together.

And anon they came to a castle and would lodge there. But a man came out of the castle and said that the custom was that ere a knight errant could have lodging he must first overthrow a knight of the castle; and thereafter he must defend the custom in like manner.

'This is a foul custom,' said Sir Dinadan, 'and meseemeth the castle is like to be foul also. For so foul a hostel I will not fight.'

By then were two knights come out of the castle, and had made them ready to joust, and Sir Tristram said to Sir Dinadan that he could not leave them with honour. Then was Sir Dinadan exceeding wroth, and in his fury he rode upon one of the knights and smote him down to the earth. And so Sir Tristram and Sir Dinadan lodged within the castle.

And anon, ere they retired to their rest, they of the castle came and told them that two knights had come and asked lodging; and now must they defend the custom of the castle.

'What array is this?' said Sir Dinadan, 'I would fain have my rest.'

'That may not be,' said Sir Tristram. 'Now must we defend the custom of this castle insomuch as we had the better of the lords of this castle. Now therefore needs must ye make ready.'

'In the devil's name', said Sir Dinadan, 'came I into your company.'

Then did Sir Tristram take Sir Dinadan by force and laced on his helm and buckled on his armour, and bade him acquit him as a good knight should.

'I will not,' said Sir Dinadan, 'for I have fought enough in getting into this castle. And for so poor a lodging I will not fight again. But ye fare as a man that were out of his mind, that would cast himself away. And I may curse the time that ever I saw you, for in all the world are not two such knights that are so wood[1] as Sir Lancelot and ye, Sir Tristram. For once I fell in the fellowship of Sir Lancelot, as I have done now with you, and he set me so to work that a quarter of a year I kept my bed. Jesu defend me from two such knights, and especially from your fellowship!'

And therewith Sir Dinadan took his horse and rode swiftly away from the castle. And thereat Sir Tristram was ashamed, and knew not what to do. And by then there was much noise of people of the castle that he and Sir Dinadan must either go or fight.

And at the last he rode away secretly by a postern. And thereafter he came to the Castle of Maidens, and there found Sir Persides; and they two went unto their lodgings.

So when they were disarmed and had refreshed themselves

[1] mad

they went to the windows of their lodging to see the knights ride to and fro towards the tournament. Then was Sir Tristram ware of a likely knight riding upon a great black horse and with a black-covered shield. And all the people cried him greeting with great joy.

'What knight is that?' said Sir Tristram.

'I know him well,' said Sir Persides, 'he is one of the best knights in the world.'

'Then it is Sir Lancelot,' said Sir Tristram.

'Nay,' said Sir Persides, 'it is Sir Palomides that is yet unchristened.'

And as Sir Palomides passed beneath the window, all the people saluted him and cried with a loud voice: 'Jesu save thee and keep thee, thou noble knight, Sir Palomides!'

And Sir Palomides was in a confusion for their praise, and hastened on his way. And anon there came a herald that cried that the joust was beginning.

Then said Sir Persides unto Sir Tristram: 'In faith Sir Palomides is a right noble knight, and many worthy deeds hath he done. But as for me I may not love him over much.'

And within a while after there came a squire from the castle that said that a knight with a black shield had smitten down thirteen knights.

'Now, fair sir,' said Sir Tristram, 'let us cast on us light cloaks, and let us go see that play.'

'Not so,' said Sir Persides, 'we will not go like knaves thither, but we will ride like men and as good knights to withstand our enemies.'

So they armed them and took their horses and great spears and thither they rode thereas many knights assayed themselves before the tournament. And anon Sir Palomides saw Sir

Persides, and then he sent a squire unto him and said: 'Go thou to yonder knight with the green shield and therein a lion of gold, and say him I require him to joust with me. And tell him that my name is Sir Palomides.'

When Sir Persides understood the request of Sir Palomides he made him ready. And then anon they met together, and Sir Persides had a fall. Then Sir Tristram dressed him[1] to be avenged on Sir Palomides. And that saw Sir Palomides and rode against him swiftly and smote him over his horse's tail. Then started up Sir Tristram, and took horse lightly, and was wroth out of measure and sore ashamed of that fall: for all the people cried out upon him and mocked at his overthrow. So then Sir Tristram sent unto Sir Palomides by Gouvernail, and prayed him to joust with him.

'Nay,' said Sir Palomides, 'as at this time I will not joust with that knight, for I know him better than he weeneth. And, if he be wroth, he may right it tomorn when he may see me and many other knights.'

So with that came Sir Dinadan who knew Sir Tristram by his horse and his great stature. And he had come but to look upon the deeds of Sir Tristram. And when he saw that which befell Sir Tristram, he began to jape and said: 'Lo, Sir Tristram, here may a man prove, be he never so good, yet he may have a fall; and he was never so wise but he might be overseen[2]; and he rideth well that never fell.'

But Sir Tristram was passing wroth, and said nought to Sir Persides and Sir Dinadan but that he would be avenged.

And then there came out a knight bearing a shield of the arms of Cornwall. And he smote down all those that came out against him.

[1] made himself ready.　[2] mistaken.

3   **Sir Bleoberis and Sir Palomides met so hard that Sir Palomides
      fell to the earth, horse and man (also Sir Tristram
      and Sir Breuse–sans–Pité)** (*see page* 111)

4   **Sir Tristram dressed Sir Palomides unto
             the fields and woods** (*see page* 124)

Then sent Sir Palomides a squire to that Cornish knight and told him that Sir Palomides would joust with him, and the knight was glad thereat. So either knight made them ready with great spears.

'By the Lord,' said Sir Tristram, he is a good knight that beareth the shield of Cornwall, and meseemeth he rideth in the best manner that ever I saw knight ride.'

'Whatsoever he be,' said Sir Dinadan, 'I warrant he is of King Ban's blood. Yet ye shall see that Sir Palomides will quit him right well.'

'It may be so,' said Sir Tristram, 'but I undertake that knight shall give him a fall.'

Right so they spurred their horses and feutred their spears, and either smote other. And Sir Palomides brake a spear on that other knight, but he sat and moved not: and he smote Sir Palomides so hard that he made his horse to avoid[1] the saddle. And the stroke brake his shield and the hauberk, and, had he not fallen, he had been slain. And right so the knight rode his way, none wist whither.

So in the morn Sir Tristram and Sir Persides rode to the field. And Sir Tristram bore the black shield that he had commanded Gouvernail to ordain him, and Sir Persides bore a shield all white without device.

And Sir Palomides rode by forest ways to the tourney, and there met him Sir Ector de Maris, that sought Sir Lancelot and proffered him to joust. And so Sir Palomides smote him horse and man to the earth and then left him. And when Sir Ector was come to himself he took his horse and rode to a fountain and there found he Sir Lancelot, that rested him there, and told him how an unknown knight upon a black

[1] throw off.

C

horse with a black shield had overthrown him. And Sir Lancelot wit well that this was Sir Palomides and told Sir Ector how he had overthrown him when he bore a shield of Cornwall. And anon they two rode to the tournament.

So when Sir Tristram and Sir Persides were come to the field, then they found that the knights of the King of Northgalis were set against the knights of Sir Carados of Scotland. And Sir Tristram and Sir Persides came upon the side of King Carados, and so they did fare that they put the knights of Northgalis aback. And by that were come King Arthur and many of his knights; and then came also Sir Lancelot and Sir Ector, but they took no part in the tournament that day.

But ever Sir Tristram ranged up and down the field until King Arthur blew to lodging. And then Sir Tristram rode unto his lodging, and with him Sir Persides and Sir Dinadan. And all the kings and lords that were judges gave the prize to the knight with the Black shield, that was Sir Tristram, but yet they knew him not.

Now Sir Palomides had watched the tournament that day, but took no part therein, and well he deemed it was Sir Tristram. So upon the morn he drew upon the part of King Arthur that was with King Carados. And Sir Palomides sent a damsel to ask Sir Tristram what was his name.

'As for that,' said he, 'tell Sir Palomides that he shall not know at this time unto the time that I have broken two spears upon him. But let him wit this: that I am the same knight that he smote down, in the evening at the jousts before the tournament, and tell him plainly on what party that he shall be, I will be of the contrary party.'

And when Sir Tristram heard that Sir Palomides should be of King Arthur's party, then said he that would be with the

King of Northgalis. And so it was and Sir Tristram did such great deeds that again, for the second day also, all they adjudged the prize to the knight with the black shield. But when King Arthur blew to lodging, then Sir Tristram, Sir Persides and Sir Dinadan rode swiftly into the forest, that no man could find them.

And as he rode through the forest, Sir Tristram came upon a knight that complained unto himself and said: 'I, woeful knight, Sir Palomides! What misadventure befalleth me that thus am defiled with falsehood and shame! God in Heaven, why forgettest thou me so, that call upon thee night and day? Yet it is not thou that dishonourest me, but Sir Tristram. Alas, why live I so long? Would that he had slain me when first in Ireland we fought together!'

And then he gat his sword in his hand and made many strange signs and tokens and vowed to slay himself. But through his raging he threw his sword away, witting not where. Then Sir Palomides wailed and wrung his hands, and at the last for pure sorrow ran into that fountain and sought after his sword. Then Sir Tristram saw that and ran upon Sir Palomides and held him in his arms fast.

'What art thou,' said Sir Palomides, 'that holdeth me so?'

'I am a man of the forest that would thee no harm.'

'Alas,' said Sir Palomides, 'I may never win worship where Sir Tristram is. And if he be away, for the most part I have the gree,[1] only that Sir Lancelot, or else Sir Lamorak be there.'

'What would ye do,' said Sir Tristram, 'an ye had Sir Tristram?'

'I would fight with him,' said Sir Palomides, 'and ease my

[1] prize for victory.

heart upon him. And yet, to say thee sooth, Sir Tristram is the gentlest knight in this world living.'

Then Sir Tristram said him such kind words, that Sir Palomides went with him to his lodging. But in no wise might Sir Tristram be known to Sir Palomides for the scars and bruises on his face that he had in the tournament and for that he spake in a feigned voice. Also Sir Palomides was nigh out of his wits. And when Sir Tristram saw that, he covertly bade Sir Persides to make him no quarrels.

And so they rode together till they came to Sir Tristram's lodging, and there had Sir Palomides all the cheer that might be had all that night, yet avowed he that he must depart ere the dawn for to be avenged upon Sir Tristram. And so he might not sleep for anguish: and in the dawning of the day he took his horse privily, and bade the servants not to awake their masters, and so rode to his own lodging that was in the midst of the plain by the Castle.

And there he found Sir Gaheris and Sir Sagramore le Desirous and right glad they were to see him. For they had seen him ride out from the tournament safe and sound, and when he returned not again they deemed him dead. But Sir Palomides excused himself and said that he had an adventure to perform, and so lay down in his armour to sleep till the tournament began.

But Sir Tristram was wroth when he heard that Sir Palomides had departed privily. Then came one that said that King Arthur would essay the jousts that day. And so he armed himself and rode to the tournament with Sir Persides.

And then upon the morn the king blew unto the tournament. And Sir Palomides and Sir Gaheris and Sir Sagramore held by the party of King Arthur. For this day was the king come into the tournament; but for the most part might he not meddle in jousts for that he was a king.

And then did Sir Palomides such mighty deeds, that the party of Northgalis and of the king of the hundred knights was put to the worse. And then came in Sir Tristram and jousted with Sir Palomides; and there by fine force Sir Tristram smote Sir Palomides over his horse's croup. And in like manner he smote down King Arthur. But by the force of King Arthur's knights the king and Sir Palomides were horsed again.

Then King Arthur with a great eager heart gat a great spear in his hand and there he smote Sir Tristram over his horse's side. Then foot-hot Sir Palomides came upon Sir Tristram to have over-ridden him. But Sir Tristram stooped a little aside and gat him by the arm and pulled him down from his horse.

Then Sir Palomides lightly arose, and they dashed together with their swords mightily. And twice Sir Tristram smote Sir Palomides a mighty stroke upon the helm saying: 'Take this! It is from your good friend, Tristram.' Yet ever Sir Palomides defended himself bravely till there came the King of the hundred knights and horsed Sir Tristram again, and said unto him that the knights of Arthur had nigh vanquished his party.

And anon Sir Palomides was horsed again, and he rode upon Sir Tristram and gave him a great dash with his sword. Then Sir Tristram gat him by his neck with his both hands and pulled him clean out of his saddle. And so he ran him a spear's length all around till he might bear him no longer, and then he let him fall at his adventure!

And thereafter Sir Tristram rode here and there and did his

great pain,[1] till at the last there encountered with him Sir Lancelot. And there they came together as thunder. And Sir Tristram's spear brake in pieces; but Sir Lancelot smote him on the side a deep wound nigh to the death. And therewithal Sir Tristram departed from the field. And that saw Sir Dinadan and followed him.

And at the tournament the king of Northgalis and the king of the hundred knights were put to the worse. And because Sir Lancelot abode and was the last in the field, the prize was given to him. But Sir Lancelot would not thereof, but would give it to Sir Tristram. But nowise could Sir Tristram be found.

So that night, the tournament being ended, King Arthur made a great feast to all that would come.

[1] made great exertions.

VIII

The Imprisonment

AND thus we let pass King Arthur, and a little we will turn unto Sir Palomides, that after he had a fall of Sir Tristram he was near hand araged out of his wit[1] for despite of Sir Tristram. And so he followed him by adventure. And as he rode in the forest, there encountered with him Sir Griflet le Fise de Dieu and King Bagdemagus. And Sir Griflet deemed him a coward knight that fled from the tournament, and so called upon him to joust, but he would not. But Sir Griflet rode upon him whether he would or no. So Sir Palomides turned, and smote Sir Griflet to the earth and in like manner he served King Bagdemagus. And he took their horses, and took off their bridles, and chased them into the forest; and so rode on his way. And as he came by a river, in his woodness[2] he would have made his horse to have leapt over the water; and the horse failed footing and fell into the river, wherefore Sir Palomides was adread lest he should have been drowned. And then he avoided his horse and swam to the land and let his horse go down by adventure. And when he came to the land he took off his harness, and sat roaring and crying as a man out of his mind.

Right so came by a damsel that was sent from Sir Gawaine unto Sir Mordred that lay sick in a castle near at hand. And she and Sir Palomides had language together that pleased

[1] demented. [2] madness.

neither of them. For she saw by his garments that he had fallen in the river, and she deemed that to be the cause of his grief, and she said: 'Sir knight, why complain ye so? Ye complain more than a gentle knight ought.'

But Sir Palomides was wroth at her coming and bade her go on her way and leave him to lament as he chose. Then she blamed him for his roughness, and he her again.

'Sir,' she said, 'as God is my witness I am more wise and more courteous than ye be.'

'Lady,' said Sir Palomides, 'as for your courtesy I had not noted it nor nought of it see I now, but your ill-speaking, that I wit well. Speak then of your courtesy to them to whom ye are courteous, but not to me. And, in faith, of your courtesy I would none. There is but one whose courtesy I would share; and an I had it I would be lord of all the world.'

'Truly,' said the damsel in wrath, 'if it were my courtesy ye shared, I would think me in the worse case.'

'Indeed,' said Sir Palomides, 'I would wish you in no better.'

And so this damsel rode her ways until she came to an old knight's place, wherein lay Sir Mordred. And there also were Sir Tristram and Sir Dinadan. And then she told them how she met with the woodest knight by adventure that ever she met withal. And when Sir Tristram heard that he bore a shield chequered white and black he knew him; for this was the shield that Sir Palomides had borne at the tournament on the last day.

And when the old knight heard Sir Tristram say so then he took a little palfrey and rode for Sir Palomides and brought him unto his own manor. And then Sir Palomides knew Sir Tristram for the knight that was in the pavilion at the tournament. Yet still he knew not that it was Sir Tristram, for he kept his face covered for his hurts and he said but little. And ever Sir Palomides railed upon the knight with the black shield, and ever he vowed vengeance upon him.

'Why did ye not take your vengeance upon him at the tournament?' said Sir Dinadan, 'And how did ye let him escape? I suppose it is hardihood that ye lack. For ofttimes have I found knights, that would never attack their foes, speak great words thereafter as was marvel to hear.'

Then was Sir Palomides sore enraged. The damsel also sought to upbraid him, but Tristram would not suffer it and drove her forth. And so abode they in the manor with the old knight Sir Darras. And ever Sir Palomides spake of vengeance.

And on a day that he spake thus, Sir Dinadan said unto him: 'What would ye do if ye chanced on Sir Tristram by adventure?'

'I would do him all honour and service in my power,' said Sir Palomides, 'for his high knighthood.'

'And if ye had him at your mercy, what would ye do?'

'I would honour him as I would honour King Arthur, for verily he surpasseth the king in chivalry as he doth me. And I would think no more of the ill-will I bore him.'

And Tristram was much moved by his generousness, and unto himself he vowed that never would he work to slay Sir Palomides: and it repented him sore that he had wrought to his dishonour.

Now it chanced that Sir Darras, the old knight, had three sons slain at the tournament. And on a day there came one that told Sir Darras that a knight with a black shield had slain his three sons, and two more had he wounded so that they were never like to help themselves. And this heard the damsel that was wroth at Sir Palomides and Sir Tristram. Covertly she came to the room of Sir Tristram and there she espied his shield, and then she showed it to Sir Darras.

'Ah Sir,' said she, 'this same is he that slew your three sons.'

Then without any tarrying Sir Darras put Sir Tristram, Sir Palomides and Sir Dinadan within a strong prison. And Sir Darras summoned forty knights that were of his own kin, and they would have slain the three knights when they had taken them, but Sir Darras would not. And meat and drink had they in that prison; but Sir Tristram fell so sore sick that scarce might he eat. And right heavy was Sir Palomides for him, and comforted him in the best wise he could.

So Sir Tristram endured then great pain, for sickness is the greatest pain a prisoner may have. For all the while a prisoner may have his health of body, he may ensure under the mercy of God and in hope of good deliverance. But when sickness toucheth a prisoner's body, then may a prisoner say all wealth is him bereft, and then hath he cause to wail and weep. Right so did Sir Tristram when sickness had undertaken him, for then he took such sorrow that he had almost slain himself.

And so they lay long time, and ever Sir Dinadan japed upon Sir Palomides for his quarrel with Sir Tristram.

'I marvel of thee, Sir Palomides,' said he, 'whether, as thou hadst Sir Tristram here, thou wouldst do none harm. For, an a wolf and a sheep were together in a prison, the wolf would suffer the sheep to be in peace. And Palomides and Tristram, could they not be in prison together without bitterness?'

And Palomides perceived that Dinadan mocked him. Wherefor he said: 'Nay, for too fiercely do they hate each other!'

'Then wit thou well,' said Sir Dinadan, 'this same is Sir

Tristram at a word, and now mayest thou do thy best with him.'

Then was Sir Palomides abashed and said little. Then said Sir Tristram to Sir Palomides: 'I will answer for both of us. No battle can there be thus in prison where our lives are at hazard, because the lord of this place hath done enough to us and well might do more.'

And so they peaced themselves.

'Lo, here you are become warm friends,' said Sir Dinadan. 'God grant that your friendship be not so hot as Lancelot and Galahalt and last not so long time.'

Then Sir Tristram laughed, but Sir Palomides bent his head in shame. Then said Sir Tristram: 'What is this bitterness that dureth so long twixt thee and me?'

'Have I not right to hate you,' said Sir Palomides, 'for all the ill ye have done me? Yet naught have I done to earn your hate.'

'That is truth,' said Sir Tristram, 'yet oft have ye made my heart sad when it was joyous. But now it is better to leave all this, and to take such joy as we may in remembering our good adventures, and the joys that we have had.'

'Easy is it for you,' said Sir Palomides, 'that have found joy when I had nought but bitter sorrow. And so, I swear, will it be to my death day.'

'Oh peace!' said Sir Dinadan, 'and let us speak of other matters.'

Then soon after this Sir Tristram fell again into his sickness, that he weened to have died. Then Sir Palomides and Sir Dinadan made great dole, so that one told Sir Darras how the mighty knight that bore the black shield was likely to die.

'That shall not be,' said Sir Darras, 'for God defend, when

knights come to me for succour, that I should suffer them to die within my prison. Therefore go fetch that sick knight and his fellows afore me.'

So then were they taken up out of the prison, and in a month was Sir Tristram made whole of his sickness. And then were they brought before Sir Darras. And Sir Darras said unto Sir Tristram:

'Sir knight, me repents of your sickness, for ye are called a full noble knight, and so it seemeth by you. And wit you well that it shall never be said that I, Sir Darras, shall destroy such a noble knight as ye are in prison, howbeit that ye have slain three of my sons, wherefore I was greatly agrieved. But now shalt thou go, and thy fellows, and take your horse and your armour, for they have been fair and clean kept and ye shall go where it liketh you upon this covenant: that thou, knight, wilt promise me to be good friend to my sons two that be now on live, and also that thou tell me thy name.'

'Sir, as for me, my name is Sir Tristram de Lyones, and in Cornwall was I born, and nephew I am unto King Mark. And as for the death of your sons I might not do withal[1]; for, as they had been the next kin that I have, I might have done none otherwise. And if I had slain them by treason or treachery, I had been worthy to have died.'

'All this I consider,' said Sir Darras, 'that all that ye did was by force of knighthood, and that was the cause I would not put you to death. But sith ye be Sir Tristram, I pray you heartily to be my good friend and my sons'.'

'Sir,' said Sir Tristram, 'I promise you by the faith of my body ever while I live I will do you service, for ye have done to us but as a natural knight ought to do.'

[1] could not help it.

Then they took their leave; and every knight took their horses and harness, and so departed; and rode together till they came to a crossway.

'Now, fellows,' said Sir Tristram, 'here will we depart in sunder.'

So they departed each his own way; and Sir Palomides rode by a fountain, whereat sat a damsel by a dead knight, making great dole. And she said to Sir Palomides that Sir Breuse-sans-pité had slain her knight; and all night long had she sat by him in hope that some life were left in him, and now she knew not where to go.

Then for pity Sir Palomides made the damsel to leap on her palfrey, and he promised to be her warrant and to help her bury her lord. And so, as they rode together by a tower, there came out Sir Breuse-sans-pité, and suddenly he struck Sir Palomides from behind that he fell from his horse. And or ever he might recover his horse Sir Breuse slew the damsel. Then was Sir Palomides sore ashamed, and fiercely assailed Sir Breuse, and put him aback. And then came out eight other knights out of the tower; and all they nine attacked Sir Palomides together that scarce might he defend himself.

And it chanced that Sir Tristram rode that way, and saw that one knight did battle with nine knights. And that one knight did so marvellously that he had unhorsed them all. Then Sir Tristram rode unto the knights and smote on the right hand and on the left hand passing sore, so that those that were left on live fled into the tower and shut fast the gate against Sir Tristram.

Then returned he unto Sir Palomides and found him sitting under a tree sore wounded: and so stricken and hewn was his shield that Sir Tristram knew it not.

'Gramercy,' said Sir Palomides, 'of your great goodness, for ye have saved me of my death.'

'What is your name?' said Sir Tristram.

'Sir, my name is Sir Palomides.'

'Ah Jesu!' said Sir Tristram, 'Thou hadst a fair grace of me this day that I should rescue thee, and thou art the man that ever showest me ill will. So now make thee ready, for I shall do battle with thee.'

'It may be so,' said Sir Palomides, 'but ye have done over much for me this day that I should fight with you. Nor none worship will it be for you to have ado with me, for ye are fresh and I am sore wounded. And therefore as ye will needs have ado with me, assign me a day, and then shall I meet you without fail.'

'Ye say well,' said Sir Tristram. 'Now I assign you to meet me this day fortnight in the meadow by the river of Camelot where Merlin set the perron.'[1]

And so they were agreed. And then Sir Tristram rode upon his way toward Cornwall. But Sir Palomides abode near by in an abbey for to be healed of his wounds.

[1] block of stone.

IX

Sir Palomides Rescues King Mark

A ND on a day after that he was healed of his wounds, as Sir Palomides rode at adventure he saw a knight come flying, and he bore the arms of Cornwall. Then said Sir Palomides: 'Return again for shame and stand with me, and I shall be thy warrant.'

'Ah, fair knight,' said the Cornish knight, 'let me pass for yonder cometh after me the best knight of the world with the black barred shield.'

'Fie, for shame!' said Sir Palomides, 'He that cometh after thee is neither Sir Lancelot nor Sir Tristram, yet even against them would I stand by thee.'

When the Cornish knight heard him say that word, he returned his horse and abode by him. And then Sir Palomides bore a spear unto the knight that came after the Cornish knight, and smote him so sore that he bore him over his horse's tail, that nigh he had broken his neck. And anon after him came a second knight, and so he and Sir Palomides hurtled together wondrous sore. And Sir Palomides smote the knight so sore that he went to the earth horse and man. And anon came four other knights, and so Sir Palomides served them all.

And then those knights sent unto Sir Palomides a squire that prayed him to tell his name.

'As for my name,' said Sir Palomides, 'tell those knights I

am a knight errant as they are, but my name they shall not wit at this time.'

So Sir Palomides rode on his way a soft pace, and the Cornish knight rode after him praising him mickle. But he would answer no words but sighed wondrous sore, hanging down his head and taking no heed to his words. Thus they rode well nigh a three mile English. And then Sir Palomides called to him a varlet that was with the Cornish knight, and bade him:

'Ride until yonder fair manor, and commend me to the lady of the castle and place, and pray her to send me some refreshing of good meats and drinks. And if she ask thee what I am, tell her that I am the knight that followeth the Questing Beast.'

Then the varlet went his way and came to the manor and saluted the lady and told her from whence he was come. And when she understood that he came from the knight that followed the Questing Beast, 'Ah, sweet Lord Jesu,' she said, 'when shall I see that gentle knight, my dear son Sir Palomides? Alas! Will he not abide with me?'

And therewith she swooned and wept and made passing great dole. But all so soon as she might she gave the varlet meat all that he asked; and then the varlet returned unto Sir Palomides, and told him all that the lady had said. And so Sir Palomides ate his meat and said nothing. And he asked not the name of the Cornish knight that was indeed King Mark, but the knight heard the varlet speak his name.

And anon the knight fell on sleep.[1] And when Sir Palomides saw him sound on sleep he took his horse and rode his way. And thereafter the knight awaked, and took his horse and

[1] asleep.

sought Sir Palomides through the forest. And at the last he found him, sighing and complaining, that he seemed nigh out of his wits. And he sat him down near at hand, but Sir Palomides saw him not.

Now turn we unto Sir Dinadan that rode his ways through the forest and found the six knights that Sir Palomides had overthrown: and they were passing heavy. These knights were Sir Dagonet, Sir Brandiles, Sir Osanna le Cure Hardi, Sir Uwaine, Sir Griflet, and Sir Agravaine; also Sir Mordred was with them. And they told Sir Dinadan how that they had dressed Sir Dagonet in the armour of Sir Mordred in despite of King Mark. And they had told King Mark that Sir Lancelot was come against him. And so King Mark fled, and Sir Dagonet after him; and they all rode to see what would chance.

And when Sir Dinadan wist how they had sped, he said: 'I dare lay thereon my head it is Sir Lamorak de Galis. I promise you all I shall find him an he may be found in this country.'

And so Sir Dinadan rode after this knight, and after it was night he heard a doleful noise as it were of a man. Then Sir Dinadan rode towards that noise, and when he came nigh that noise he alit off his horse and went near him on foot. Then was he ware of a knight that sat under a tree and his horse tied by him and his helm off; and ever that knight made a doleful complaint as ever made knight and always he complained of La Beale Iseult, the queen of Cornwall, and said:

'Ah, fair lady, why love I thee? For thou art fairest of all other, and as yet showedst thou me never love nor bounty. Perdie, and yet, alas, must I love thee! And I may not blame thee, fair lady, for mine eyes caused me. The falsest knight and king of the world is your husband, and the most coward and full of treason is your lord King Mark. And alas! so beauteous a lady and peerless of all other should be matched with the most villainous knight of the world!'

And all this language heard King Mark, what Sir Palomides said by him. Wherefore he were adread, when he saw Sir Dinadan, lest that he had espied him, and that he would tell Sir Palomides that he was King Mark.

Then went Sir Dinadan unto Sir Palomides, and said:

'Sir knight, I praise God that I have not your sort of love, that is bitter as the snake's venom. But the love I bear in my heart makes me ever gay and joyous, nor do I think whether my lady be hot or cold. For nothing I ask save that I know I can obtain. And never would I give my love to this Iseult; for so many hearts has she in her belly, great and marvellous and mighty, that they would never let mine stay there but would chase it out. The hearts of Tristram and Palomides are too proud and fierce to share any woman's belly with mine. So I keep mine to myself, and will give it to no woman. And in faith, with those hearts she has, the mighty heart of Tristram will drive out the false and coward heart of Mark, and after that it will be the turn of Palomides' heart. Nay, sir, ye would have ado with a knight too big for you.'

Never had Palomides heard language the like of this, and he kept silence.

'How, sir knight,' said Sir Dinadan, 'will ye not argue in your own cause?'

'I pray you,' said Sir Palomides, 'say no more. For ye will drive me out of my senses.'

'That may not be,' said Sir Dinadan, 'for never had ye any

sense to be in, or else ye would not be so unhappy. And pity it is that so good a knight hath so little measure.'

'Who be ye,' said Sir Palomides, 'that talk in this fashion?'

And when he knew that it was Sir Dinadan, he was right glad and bade him welcome. And Sir Dinadan asked pardon for that he had said.

And then Sir Palomides was ware of King Mark, but dimly for that it was dark, and he knew him not. Then Palomides asked what he thought of love.

And King Mark said: 'Verily, I would love lightly, as this knight here. Yet are they not to be blamed that are swayed by great passion, for their nature drives them; and so it was with the wisest of men, even Solomon.'

Then were Sir Palomides and Sir Dinadan well pleased with this answer. And Sir Dinadan told Sir Palomides how that Sir Tristram and Sir Lancelot fought a great battle at the perron of Merlin, and that Sir Tristram had the better.

'Sir Tristram I deem the better knight,' said Sir Palomides, 'for he hath greater strength and more cunning than Sir Lancelot. But it repents me that I failed of my tryst at the perron with Sir Tristram, for a full month I lay wounded in an abbey ere I might move from my bed.'

'Nay, repent not,' said Sir Dinadan, 'for it was thy good fortune. For never would ye have vanquished him.'

So after a little while Sir Palomides and Sir Dinadan slept. And then King Mark withdrew him, and took his horse and rode as fast as he might unto Camelot.

And on the morn when they awaked they found the knight gone. And then Sir Dinadan told Sir Palomides of the great tournament that should be at Camelot, and that there should be Queen Guinevere and Queen Iseult. Also he told him how

Sir Tristram was made knight of the Round Table, and sat in the siege of Sir Marhalt.

'Wit you well, sir knight,' said Sir Palomides, 'for the love of La Beale Iseult I will be there, but I will not have ado in King Arthur's court.'

And so they dressed on their helms and put on their shields and mounted upon their horses and took the broad way towards Camelot. And then were they ware of a castle that was fair and rich and also passing strong as any was within this realm.

So Sir Dinadan said to Sir Palomides:

'Here is a castle that I know well and therein dwelleth Queen Morgan le Fay, King Arthur's sister. And King Arthur gave her this castle, by the which he hath repented him sithen a thousand times; for sithen King Arthur and she have been at debate and strife. And no other castle hath she now in Logres; but this castle could he never get nor win of her by no manner of engine.[1] And now hath she a custom that there shall no knight pass this way but he must joust with one or with two or with three. And if he be a knight of King Arthur's and be beaten, he shall lose his horse and harness and all that he hath, and hard if he[2] escape but that he shall be made prisoner. But an Sir Lancelot should come, then will all the knights of the castle attack him together. And only if he be slain will she leave this custom.'

'So God help me,' said Sir Palomides, 'this is a shameful and villainous usage for a queen to use, and with all my heart I will destroy that shameful custom. And if she send out any knights, as I suppose she will, to joust, they shall have both their hands full.'

[1] means.   [2] he is unlikely to.

'And I shall not fail you,' said Sir Dinadan, 'unto my puissance,[1] upon my life.'

[1] power.

X

The Japes of Sir Dinadan

Now as they stood on horseback afore the castle, there came a knight with a green shield, and two squires after him. And he came straight unto Sir Palomides, and said:

'Fair knight errant, I require thee for the love thou owest unto knighthood that thou wilt not have ado with the men of this castle. For I came hither to seek this deed and it is my quest. And therefore I beseech you, sir knight, let me deal; and if I be beaten, revenge me.'

'In the name of God,' said Sir Palomides, 'let see how ye will speed, and we shall behold you.'

Then anon came forth a knight of the castle and proffered to joust; and the knight with the green shield smote him so hard that he bore him over to the earth. And so he served a second and a third. Then came Sir Palomides and besought him that he might help him to joust.

'Now, sir knight,' said he, 'suffer me at this time to have my will; for an they were twenty knights, I shall not doubt[1] them.'

And ever there were upon the walls of the castle many lords that cried and said: 'Well have ye jousted, knight with the green shield!'

And then came out a fourth and a fifth; and the knight with the green shield smote them down until he had van-

[1] fear.

quished twelve knights. But as soon as the knight had smitten
them down, his squires took their horses and voided their
saddles and bridles of the horses, and turned them into the
forest; and made the knights to be kept to the end of the
jousts. And then Sir Palomides said to Sir Dinadan: 'To see
this knight smitten down, we must wait until the day of
judgment.'

And so he went to him again and prayed him that he would
let him joust until he was refreshed.

'Why, sir,' said the knight, 'seems you that I am weak and
feeble? Methinketh ye proffer me great wrong and shame
where I do well maybe, for I tell you now as I told you erst;
an there were twenty knights, I shall beat them; an I be
beaten or slain, then may ye revenge me. And if ye think that
I be weary and ye have an appetite to joust with me, I shall
find you jousting enough.'

'Nay, sir,' said Sir Palomides, 'I said it not to your dishonour. But meseemeth ye have overmuch on hand, and
fain am I too for two or three jousts.'

'An ye were gentle,' said the knight, 'ye would proffer me
no shame. But since you have such a craving to joust, leave
these feeble knights and joust with me. For so I require you.'

'Sith ye require me,' said Sir Palomides, 'take keep to[1]
yourself. Yet little honour will I get if I beat you that cannot
now be so fresh as at first.'

Then was the knight wroth and bade him keep himself.
And then they two came together as fast as their horses might
run, and the knight smote Sir Palomides so sore through the
shield that the spear went into his side and hurt him a great
wound and perilous. And therewith Sir Palomides avoided

[1] guard.

his saddle. And then that knight turned unto Sir Dinadan, and Sir Dinadan cried out that he would not joust, but the other spared not and came straight upon him. So Dinadan for shame put forth his spear and all to-brast it upon the knight; but he smote Sir Dinadan so hard that he bore him from his horse. But he would not suffer his squires to meddle with their horses because they were knights errant.

Then came a knight unarmed out of the castle and said: 'Knight with the green shield, overmuch damage have ye done this same day. And therefore return whither ye will, for here are no more that will have ado with you. For we repent sore that ever ye came here, for by thee is fordone[1] the old custom of this castle.'

And so he returned within the castle and shut fast the gates. Then the knight with the green shield turned and called his squire, and so past forth on his way and rode at a great pace.

And when he was past Sir Palomides said:

'I had never such shame of one knight that ever I met for to be beaten by one that is not Tristram nor Lancelot. And therefore will I ride after him to be revenged upon him with my sword, for on horseback I deem I shall get no worship of him.'

'Sir Palomides,' said Sir Dinadan, 'where is thy courtesy? In truth grief hath taken away your sense. For the knight is passing weary and shame it would be to have ado with him.'

'By Almighty Jesu,' said Sir Palomides, 'I shall never be at ease else!'

So Sir Palomides mounted his horse and rode after the knight, and Sir Dinadan followed after. And down in a valley beside a fountain they were ware where he was alit to repose

---

[1] to put an end to.

him, and had done off[1] his helm for to drink at the well. Then Sir Palomides rode fast till he came nigh him, and then he said: 'Knight, remember ye me, and of the same deed that ye did to me late at the castle. Therefore redress thee, for I will have ado with thee.'

'Fair knight,' said he, 'of me ye win no worship, for ye have seen this day that I have been travailed sore.'

'As for that,' said Sir Palomides, 'I will not let: for, wit you well, I will be revenged.'

'Well,' said the knight, 'I may happen to endure you.'

And therewith Sir Palomides alit down on foot and dressed his shield before him and pulled out his sword. And then they came together a soft pace, and wonderly they lashed together passing thick the mountenance[2] of an hour or ever they breathed. Then they traced and traversed and waxed wonderly wroth, and either behight other[3] death. They hewed so fast with their swords that they cut down half their shields; and they hewed together on helms and mails that the bare flesh in some places stood above their harness. But at the last Sir Palomides waxed faint by cause of his first wound that he had at the castle with the spear, for that wound grieved him wonderly sore.

'Now, fair knight,' said Sir Palomides, 'meseemeth we have essayed either other passingly well, and if it may please you I require you of your knighthood to tell me your name.'

'Sir,' he said, 'that is me right loth, for ye have done me great wrong and no knighthood to proffer me battle, considering my great travail. But, an ye will tell me your name, I wist tell you mine.'

'Sir, wit you well, my name is Sir Palomides.'

[1] doffed. [2] space. [3] threatened the other with.

'Then, sir, ye shall understand that my name is Sir Lamorak de Galis, son and heir me to the good knight and king, King Pellinore; and Sir Tor, the good knight, is my half-brother.'

When Sir Palomides had heard him say so, he kneeled down and asked mercy: 'For outrageously have I done to you this day, considering the great deeds of arms I have seen you do, and shamefully and unknightly I have required you to do battle with me.'

'Ah, Sir Palomides,' said Sir Lamorak, 'overmuch have ye done and said to me!'

And therewith he pulled him up with both his hands and said: 'Sir Palomides, worthy knight, in all this land there is no better than ye be nor more of prowess; and me repents sore that we should fight together.'

'So it doth not me,' said Sir Palomides, 'and yet I am sorer wounded than ye be; but, as for that, I shall soon be whole. But certainly I would not, for the fairest castle in the land, but that you and I had met: for I shall love you the days of my life afore all other knights except my brother Sir Safere.'

'I say the same', said Sir Lamorak, 'except my brother Sir Tor.'

Then came Sir Dinadan and he made great joy of Sir Lamorak. Then their squires dressed both their shields and their harness, and stopped their wounds. And thereby at a priory they rested them all night.

And on the morn they took their horses and rode till they saw a fair castle that stood on a mountain. And thither they rode, and found therein Galahalt the Haut Prince, and there they had great cheer and were well eased. And on the morrow Sir Lamorak asked Sir Dinadan what he would do.

'Sir, I will tomorrow to the court of King Arthur.'

'By my head,' said Sir Palomides, 'I will not ride this three days; for I am sore hurt and much have I bled, and therefore I will repose me here.'

'Truly,' said Sir Lamorak, 'and I will abide here with you, unless that ye tarry overlong.'

So Sir Dinadan took his horse and departed from them.

And as he rode, there met him a knight that said: 'Sir knight, it behoves you to joust with me.'

'Know ye no way but this, sir knight,' said Dinadan, 'to salute a knight errant? God save me, but it is scant courtesy! And how know ye whether it suits me to joust or no?'

'Certes,' said the knight, 'I know not. But I know that it is fitting for me to joust with you.'

And Sir Dinadan smiled and said: 'Then tell me, this joust that ye ask, do ye want it for love or for hate of me?'

'In truth,' said the knight, 'I ask it not in hate, but in true friendship and for sport.'

'I find not this friendship very friendly, nor such sport much of a game. Proffer your friendship to some other, for I would rather be your enemy if such is your friendship.'

'How is this?' said the knight, 'Do ye refuse my challenge?'

'Yea indeed,' said Sir Dinadan, 'for ye challenge me friendly, and I hold me your enemy.'

'How may that be?' said the knight, 'For no harm have I done you, nor ever erst, methinketh, have I met with you.'

'Your remembrance accords with mine,' said Sir Dinadan. 'But wit you well I will not hold you for friend, and I will not accord with you for that which pleases me not, for this language that we have had together wearieth me.'

'In the name of God,' said the knight, 'since ye yourself say that ye are mine enemy, I challenge you to joust with better will than ever I had. Be on your guard against me, for I will slay you if ever the chance come.'

'Good sir,' said Sir Dinadan, 'I perceive that ye would fight on whatsoever cause. But let us act wisely in this, for well ye wit that the enmity of knights is some time for some great cause and some time for but a little thing. But now ye know not for what cause I hate you, nor will I at this time declare it. And therefore let us take our matter to King Arthur that can judge between us.'

But the knight knew not that he spake mockingly and asked him his name. And when he knew that it was Sir Dinadan, he was somewhat abashed how it would end; and he prayed Sir Dinadan that he would not turn it ill for him.

'Nay,' said Sir Dinadan, 'for I count this chivalry the best thing in the world if only I can take no part in it.'

'What, Sir Dinadan,' said the knight, 'do ye not wish to maintain the customs of Logres? Are ye not knight errant?'

'Yea, in truth,' said Sir Dinadan, 'but there is overmuch jousting, and no words know knight errants save only this—"Keep yourself against me!" And so I go about refusing the challenge whenever I meet a knight errant. But, if fight I must, I defend myself as I can by word or deed.'

And so they parted, and Sir Dinadan went to King Arthur and told him of the battle between Sir Lamorak and Sir Palomides. Now King Arthur had let cry a tournament, and anon came Lamorak, and did marvellous deeds. But Sir Palomides came not, for he was not yet whole. Also the king made accord between King Mark and Sir Tristram, and they two departed into Cornwall with Queen Iseult. And Sir Lancelot and Sir Dinadan were wroth for well they knew King Mark and his treachery, and they feared for Sir Tristram.

And when the tournament was ended, Sir Dinadan took his horse and departed from the court, and rode to find Sir Palomides. And as he rode, there encountered with him Sir Breuse-sans-Pité, that had smitten down Sir Agravaine and Sir Mordred. And Sir Dinadan with pure strength smote him over his horse's tail, and rescued the two knights. But little thanks he had of it, for Gawaine and all his brethren hated Sir Dinadan because he was friend to Sir Lamorak, whose father, King Pellinore, they had slain traitorously.

And so Sir Dinadan rode to the castle where he had left Sir Palomides, And the castle hight Beale Valet. And the Haut Prince had given it to Sir Palomides. And Sir Dinadan found Sir Palomides not yet whole of the wound that Sir Lamorak gave him. And then Sir Dinadan told Sir Palomides all the tidings that he heard and saw of Sir Tristram, and how he was gone with King Mark, and with him had all his will and desire. Therewith Sir Palomides waxed wroth, for he loved La Beale Iseult, and then he wist well that Sir Tristram enjoyed her.

Now it chanced on a day that a wounded knight was borne to the castle to be healed of his wounds. And when Sir Palomides beheld him he knew him for his brother, Sir Safere. And great joy had each of other. And Sir Safere told how that he had rescued a maiden at the Bise Rock from a villain knight hight Margot Le Roux and had slain him. And thereafter by ill chance he had encountered with Sir Lancelot, and each knew not other. And Sir Lancelot hurt him sore. So stayed Sir Palomides and Sir Safere in that castle till that they were healed; and Sir Dinadan abode with them.

XI

The Coming of Igraine the Fair

IT befell on a day that Sir Galahalt, the Haut Prince, Lord of the country of Surluse, came to King Arthur's Court and asked leave to cry a jousts with the king's good will.

'I will give you leave,' said King Arthur, 'but wit you well I may not be there myself.'

'Sir,' said Queen Guinevere, 'please it you to give me leave to be at that jousts.'

'With a right good will,' said King Arthur, 'for Sir Galahalt, the good Prince, shall have you in governance. And take with you such knights as liketh you best.'

So anon she commanded Sir Lancelot to make him ready with such knights as he thought best.

So in every good town and castle of this land was made a cry that in the country of Surluse Prince Galahalt should make a jousts that should last seven days, and how the Haut Prince with the help of Queen Guinevere's knights should joust against all manner of men that cometh. When this cry was known, kings and princes, dukes and earls and barons and noble knights made them ready to be at that jousts.

So when at the end of the first day the Haut Prince blew to lodging, there came to him a damsel and complained that there was a knight that hight Sir Corsabrin that withheld all her lands. And at the court of King Arthur no champion had she found, for the best part of his knights were at the jousts.

Then there came a varlet to her and said: 'Damsel, will ye do after me?'[1]

'Full fain,' said the damsel.

'Then go ye unto such a knight that lieth here beside in an hermitage, and that knight followeth the Questing Beast: and pray him to take the battle upon him.'

So anon she took her palfrey, and within a while she found that knight, that was Sir Palomides. And when she required him, he armed him and rode with her to the Haut Prince, and he gave leave for the battle. And the damsel gave Sir Palomides a pensell[2] that he should defend for her sake. So then Sir Palomides sent unto Sir Corsabrin to tell him that, an he could win the pensell, he might have the damsel and her lands.

And this damsel cast great love upon Sir Palomides and prayed him to be her knight. And to quiet her he said that he would go to the tournament and there fight in her name. And the damsel was called Igraine the Fair.

So upon the second day, Sir Palomides came to the jousts and on his shield he bore the Questing Beast: and he challenged all knights, save only Sir Lancelot. Then the Haut Prince let cry that what knight somever smote down Sir Palomides should have his damsel to himself.

And anon Prince Galahalt met with Sir Palomides: and they came so hard together that their spears all to-shivered.[3] But Sir Galahalt smote him so hard that he bore him backward over his horse, yet lost he not his stirrups. Then they pulled out their swords and lashed together many sad[4] strokes, that many worshipful knights left their business to behold them. And at the last Sir Galahalt smote a stroke of might unto Sir Palomides sore upon the helm; but the helm was so hard that

[1] do as I tell you. [2] small pennon. [3] broke in pieces. [4] heavy.

the sword might not bite, but slipped and smote off the head of his horse.

But when Sir Galahalt saw the good knight, Sir Palomides, fall to the earth, he was ashamed of that stroke. And therewithal he alit down off his own horse and prayed Sir Palomides to take that horse of his gift, and to forgive him that deed.

'Sir,' said Palomides, 'I thank you of your great goodness. For ever of a man of worship a knight shall never have disworship.'[1]

And so he mounted upon that horse, and the Haut Prince had another horse anon.

'Now,' said the Haut Prince, 'I release to you that maiden, for ye have won her.'

'Ah,' said Sir Palomides, 'the damsel and I be at your commandment.'

And all that day none might stand against Sir Palomides. And at the last the queen and Sir Lancelot let blow[2] to lodging. So Sir Palomides came with his damsel to the lodging that the Haut Prince had appointed them, and there unarmed him.

And on the third day were many great deeds done and by adventure Sir Palomides met with Sir Blamore de Ganis, and either smote other with great spears that both horses and men fell to the earth. But Sir Blamore had such a fall that he had almost broke his neck, for the blood burst out at the nose, mouth, and ears. And then they blew to lodging and unarmed them and went to the feast.

Right so came in Sir Dinadan and made his obeisance to the queen. Then said the queen to Sir Dinadan: 'In good faith, little enough have I seen of thee at this tournament.'

[1] disgrace.   [2] ordered (the trumpets) to blow.

'My lady,' said he, 'ye are the "Abbess" of this nunnery here, and well I wit every day can ye see me if ye but look in your own heart. For when I came, Abbess and nuns were so pale that they were praying for me all day; or else they would look as though they ate nought but herbs and beans. Yet, since my coming, see how rosy ye all are, and what a little male flesh can do in a nunnery!'

'Ha Dinadan,' said she, 'and what prayer must we say for you?'

'That God keep me from the prison of lady or maiden!'

'How say ye?' said the queen. 'Would ye not have the love of a fair lady and do jousts in her honour? Ye should have been a priest!'

'Lady,' said Sir Dinadan, 'were I a priest, I would give you such absolution as ye would not ask a better, sobeit I had you in a private place'.

And all that were there laughed at Sir Dinadan, but the queen and Sir Lancelot hid somewhat their laughter.

So anon after they had dined there came a varlet bearing four spears on his back and he came to Sir Palomides and said thus: 'Here is a knight by, that hath sent the choice of four spears, and requireth you for your lady's sake to take the one half of these spears and joust with him in the field.'

'Tell him,' said Sir Palomides, 'I will not fail him.'

So Queen Guinevere, the Haut Prince, and Sir Lancelot were set in scaffolds[1] that they might give judgment of these two knights.

Then Sir Palomides and the strange knight ran together, and brake their spears to their hands. And anon either took another spear and shivered them in pieces. And then either

[1] raised platforms.

D

took a great spear, and the knight smote down Sir Palomides, horse and man. And as he would have passed over him, the knight's horse stumbled and fell down upon Sir Palomides. Then they drew their swords and lashed together wonderly sore.

Then the Haut Prince and Sir Lancelot said they saw never two knights fight better. But ever the strange knight doubled his strokes and put Sir Palomides somewhat aback. And therewithal the Haut Prince cried: 'Whoa!'

And then they went to lodging; and, when they were unarmed, anon they knew him for Sir Lamorak. And Sir Lancelot and the queen were right glad at his coming.

Now on the fourth day there came Sir Safere, Sir Palomides' brother, and with him four knights, whose lands were taken by Sir Carados of the Dolorous Tower. Also Sir Safere told him of the Earl de la Planche that had made war on their father and mother.

'And,' said he, 'I appelled[1] him before King Arthur, and there I slew him in plain battle. But here come I, seeking thine aid in the cause of these four knights, for little would King Arthur do for them.'

'That is pity,' said Sir Palomides, 'that so good a king as he was will no more aid knights in distress. But gladly will I go with thee when this jousts is ended.'

'Ah brother,' said Safere, 'and I would well also that ye become Christian man and be baptized.'

'That I will not do as at this time,' said Sir Palomides.

So they went into the field, and the damsel with them. For the Haut Prince gave leave that Sir Safere should help Sir Palomides in defence of the damsel. And Sir Palomides

[1] accused.

encountered with Sir Bleoberis, and either smote other down. In the same way did Sir Safere and Sir Ector; and the two couples did battle on foot, and never were there four knights more evenly matched. And anon they were departed and had unto their lodging and unarmed; and so they went to the great feast.

Now on the fifth day there came Sir Corsabrin unto Surluse where the Haut Prince was, and there he found Sir Palomides, the which had the pensell. And first he uttered threats, saying that he was son of Sir Aristot (whom thereafter Sir Percival slew) and boasting of his might, to the end that he might have the pensell through fear. And when this availed not, he besought Sir Palomides to give it him of his good favour, and promised him his sister in marriage and a goodly city in the heathen land. But Sir Palomides wanted not his sister, nor yet his land. And when Sir Corsabrin saw that by other means he might not have the pensell, he challenged him to battle.

'Well,' said the Haut Prince, 'this day must noble knights joust, and at after dinner we shall see how ye can do.'

Then they blew to jousts. And that day Sir Dinadan did great deeds, for he was a good knight, but ever a great scoffer and japer. And when the Haut Prince saw his deeds, he sent to Sir Lancelot and for a jest bade him strike down Sir Dinadan and bring him prisoner before the queen and him.

And so he did. And when the Haut Prince blew to lodging, then was Sir Dinadan brought prisoner before him. And the queen and the Haut Prince laughed so at Sir Dinadan that they might not stand.

'Well,' said Sir Dinadan, 'yet have I no shame, for the old shrew Sir Lancelot smote me down.'

And so the Haut Prince commanded that they should go to dinner.

'Ah,' said Sir Dinadan, 'now I perceive that I, being taken and found in good condition, am to be served to the wolf to be eaten.' For so Dinadan called the Haut Prince that was a great eater of meat.

So when dinner was done, they blew to the field to behold Sir Palomides and Sir Corsabrin. Sir Palomides pyght[1] his pensell in middes[2] of the field; and then they hurtled together with their spears as it were thunder, and they smote either other to the earth. And then they pulled out their swords, and dressed their shields and lashed together mightily as mighty knights, that well nigh there was no piece of harness[3] would hold them, for this Corsabrin was a passing felonious knight. Then Corsabrin said: 'Sir Palomides, wilt thou release me yonder damsel and the pensell?'

And so saying, being wroth out of measure, he gave Sir Palomides such a buffet that he kneeled on his knee. Then Sir Palomides arose lightly and smote him upon the helm that he fell at full length to the earth. And therewithal he raced[4] off his helm and said: 'Yield thee, Corsabrin, or thou shalt die!'

'Fie on thee,' said Corsabrin, 'and do thy worst!'

Then he smote off his head. And therewithal came a black smoke and a stink of his body, when the soul departed, that there might nobody abide the savour: and all they understood thereby that the devil carried away his soul. So was the corpus had away and buried in a wood, for he was a paynim.[5]

Then they blew unto lodging; and Sir Palomides was

[1] pitched, planted.   [2] the middle.   [3] armour.   [4] pulled.
[5] heathen.

unarmed, and went to dinner with Queen Guinevere, with
the Haut Prince and with Sir Lancelot.

'Sir,' said the Haut Prince, 'here have ye seen this day a
great miracle by Corsabrin, what savour there was when the
soul departed from the body. Therefore we all require you to
take the baptism upon you, and then all knights will say more
worship by you.'

'Sir,' said Sir Palomides, 'I wot that ye all know that into
this land I came to be christened, and christened will I be.
But I have made such a vow that I may not be christened till
I have done seven true battles for Jesus' sake, and then will I
be christened. And I trust that God will take mine intent, for
I mean truly.'

'Ah, Sir Palomides,' said Sir Dinadan, 'methinketh all thine
intent is to La Beale Iseult, and not to the Lord God.'

But Sir Palomides answered him not; but prayed Queen
Guinevere and the Haut Prince to sup with him; and also
both Sir Lancelot and Sir Lamorak, and many other good
knights.

So on the morn that was the sixth day they heard their
mass, and blew to the field, and then many worshipful knights
made them ready. And this day, there came in Sir Aglovale
and Sir Durnor, brethren to Sir Lamorak, and did right
worshipfully; but in the end they were smitten to the earth
both. And when Sir Lamorak saw his two brethren down, he
was wroth out of measure, and he gat a great spear and smote
down knights on the left hand and on the right, until his
spear brake; and then he smote down others with his sword.
Then he horsed his brethren again and said:

'Brethren, ye ought to be ashamed to fall so off your
horses! What is a knight but when he is on horseback? For I

set naught by a knight when he is on foot; for all battles on foot are but pyllours'[1] battles. For there should no knight fight on foot but if it were for treason, or else he were driven by force to fight on foot. Therefore, brethren, sit fast in your saddles, or else fight never more afore me!'

And so they blew to lodging, and the knights unarmed them and went to dinner. And therewithal came in Sir Dinadan and beheld the Haut Prince that him seemed wroth with some fault that he saw. And it was that he had a condition that he loved no fish; and because it was a Friday and he was served with fish and hated it, therefore he was not merry. Then Sir Dinadan espied where was a fish with a great head, and anon he gat it between two dishes and served the Haut Prince with that fish. And then he said: 'Sir Galahalt, well may I liken you to a wolf, for he will never eat fish, but flesh. And ill cheer maketh he at sight of fish.'

'And ye, Dinadan,' said Sir Galahalt, 'are, methinks, a fisherman's spawn, seeing the honour ye do to the fish.'

'Better a fisher than a wolf for a father,' said Sir Dinadan.

'Fish indeed ye might be,' said Sir Lancelot, 'and I warrant me ye shall leave your skin at this tournament.'

'Well, well,' said Sir Dinadan, 'what the devil do ye in this country? For here may no man win worship because of thee.'

'I ensure thee, Sir Dinadan,' said Sir Lancelot, 'I shall no more meet with thee neither with thy great spear. For I may not sit in my saddle when thy spear hitteth me.'

'An I shall be happy,' said Sir Dinadan, 'I shall beware of thy boysteous[2] body that thou bearest, and make good watch for thee ever. God forbid that ever we meet but it be at a dish of meat!'

[1] robbers'. [2] rough, strong.

Then laughed the queen and the Haut Prince that they scarce might sit at the table, and thus they made great joy.

Then on the morn of the seventh day they heard mass and blew to the field. And Queen Guinevere and all the estates[1] were set as judges, armed clean with their shields to keep the right. And many knights did many noble deeds deeds that day.

Then by all assent they gave Sir Lancelot the prize. The next was Sir Lamorak de Galis, the third was Sir Palomides, and the fourth was King Bagdemagus. And there was great joy and great nobelay[2] in all the court. And on the morn Queen Guinevere and Sir Lancelot departed unto King Arthur. But in no wise Sir Lamorak would not go with them though they besought him; for well he knew he might not trust Sir Gawaine and his brethren, that would do him ill by treachery.

[1] orders (of knighthood).   [2] pomp.

XII

The Castle of Dreams

So Sir Palomides and Sir Safere departed, and with them rode Igraine the Fair. And Sir Palomides liked her well, yet was his heart overfull of La Beale Iseult. And so he spake but little. And Sir Safere spoke to the damsel in courtly wise, but she answered him only yea or nay, and ever she gazed covertly upon Sir Palomides, and yearned after him in her heart.

And when evening was come, they were fain for a lodging for the night. And as they rode they came to the house of a vavasour[1] that received them kindly and welcomed them in and set food and drink before them. And when they had eaten and drunk their fill the damsel Igraine took leave of them and departed to her chamber.

'Brother Sir Palomides,' said Sir Safere, 'I marvel that ye who always live alone now ride in the company of this damsel.'

'In truth,' said Sir Palomides, 'I won her, as ye know, at the tournament, and an ill thing it would be to leave her by the wayside far from her own country.'

'Then what is your intent towards her,' said Sir Safere, 'for I perceive that we do not journey towards her country?'

'That is truth,' said Sir Palomides, 'and would that I knew what were best to do with her. For she is a fair maiden and a

[1] gentleman.

gentle, and glad I am of her company. Yet an end there must be.'

'If ye be so glad of her company, it behoveth you to show it with fair words, and not to ride ever in silence as though ye were alone.'

'Ye say sooth, brother,' said Sir Palomides, 'yet is my heart torn in twain; and when I would speak with her I know not what to say.'

Then anon they went to their rest, and on the morrow they arose betimes and set forth on their way. And Sir Palomides greeted Igraine fairly, yet thereafter he fell again on silence. And when Sir Safere saw that, he fell a little behind with the damsel and spake of the trees and the flowers by the way.

And when Sir Safere saw that Sir Palomides was afar off and heeded them not, he said:

'Lady, my brother, Sir Palomides, has some great matter on his mind, methinks, and heeds us not. Wherefore I would that ye tell me whether ye are content so to ride with us, and whereto ye would go.'

'I am content,' said she.

'Nay, Madam, but ye have answered but the half of my question,' said Sir Safere.

'Must this journey have an end?' said Igraine. 'I am content to ride as my lord, Sir Palomides wills.'

And Sir Safere was troubled at her saying. For well he wot that the lady Igraine loved his brother, and he wist that Sir Palomides' heart was set upon La Beale Iseult. And he knew not what to say. And then he saw where a knight came towards them all armed, bearing a great spear; and a squire rode with him. And then Sir Palomides made him ready to joust. And when the stranger knight saw that he stood stock still and called to the squire. And then he gave the squire his spear and his shield. And Sir Palomides was astonished and hoved[1] still. So then the knight rode forward again at a gentle pace; and as he came to Sir Palomides he put off his helmet and they saw that it was Sir Dinadan. And by that[2] the lady Igraine and Sir Safere were come, and right glad were they to see Sir Dinadan, and each greeted other fair.

'Nevertheless,' said Sir Palomides, 'I marvel that ye would not joust with me.'

'Why should I joust with you?' said Sir Dinadan, 'for I knew you by your arms, and ye are a better jouster than I am, as ye have but now proved at the tournament when we all have had our fill of jousting. And as for me, I have hit the earth often enough in these days, and greater comfort I find it to sit still upon my horse if I may not sit upon a chair.'

'Fie, Sir Dinadan,' said Sir Safere, 'have ye no reverence for the laws of chivalry?'

'Yea indeed,' said Sir Dinadan. 'When a knight must fight in a just quarrel. But this jousting when there is no quarrel at all, and oft times a knight errant knoweth not with whom he jousts, I hold to be a law of apes and not of men.'

'And yet,' said Sir Palomides, 'ye journey as a knight errant, as we do, seeking adventure. Why sit ye not at home until ye be summoned to a tournament or to fight in a just cause?'

'That is well asked,' said Sir Dinadan, 'and to sit at home is my desire. But I was, as ye know, at the tournament, and thereafter I must needs ride awhile with Sir Tristram. And I cannot sit at home until I be come there. And to come there I must needs ride this mare's son day by day, that bears me

[1] remained.   [2] by that time.

thither. But since in this country no road runs straight, and on every path lurk wood knights such as ye that would unhorse me, I wit not well when I may arrive.'

'Then let us bear you company,' said Sir Palomides, 'since peradventure we may defend you from such as would joust with you, and so bring you the more speedily to your journey's end.'

'Gramercy,' said Sir Dinadan, 'but how say you? For ye go one way and I another, and I would not turn you from your purpose.'

'Nay,' said Sir Safere, 'we journey but as knights errant, as Sir Palomides has said, and all roads are alike to us.'

'What!' said Sir Dinadan, 'Has your journey no end? Will ye wander along these paths until some strong knight overthrows you so that ye must lie in an abbey to be healed of your wounds or until ye are lost in the forest of Broceliande?'

'We ride with Sir Palomides,' said Sir Safere, 'and he it is that ye should ask.'

'Sir Palomides has proffered me the company of you all,' said Sir Dinadan, 'and therefore let us turn our steps for this night to yonder castle upon an hill. And there we may talk further of our journey.'

So when they were come to the castle they found it all shut up, and no sign was there of the people of the castle. And then they looked and beheld a great bronze shield, and by it a mighty hammer.

'If we would find lodging in this place,' said Sir Dinadan, 'it were well to awake them that keep it.'

So then he took hold of the hammer, but in no wise might he lift it. And then he looked upon the hammer and saw thereon a writing. And the manner of it was in this wise: 'No man may wield me save one of the four best knights in the world.'

'That am not I,' said Sir Dinadan, 'but meseemeth this is one of the stratagems of that old fox, Merlin, or perchance of Queen Morgan le Fay. And by my counsel we will not meddle but will seek other lodging.'

'Nay,' said Sir Safere, 'if an adventure come to us we must undertake it. And though I know I am not among the best knights that are now on live, yet will I essay to wield the hammer.'

But Sir Safere fared no better than Sir Dinadan. Then he called to Sir Palomides, but Sir Palomides would not. Then the Lady Igraine went to him and said:

'Sir, I mind me at the late tournament there was no knight did more than ye did. And albeit Sir Tristram was not there, none but Sir Lancelot and Sir Lamorak could stand against you. Wherefore I deem you to be one of the four best knights of the world without gainsay. Also I am weary and would rest in this castle, and for my sake I bid you essay it.'

Then Sir Palomides took the hammer in his hands and heaved at it and swung it, and smote the shield in the midst. And the sound of it rang through the country like a great church bell. And anon the door of the castle sprang open of its own accord.

'Now am I sure,' said Sir Dinadan, 'that this castle is bewitched.'

'Fear not,' said Igraine, 'for I wis that no harm shall befall us. And I pray you, Sir Dinadan, that ye will come with me within the castle. And if we meet no mischance within the space of half an hour, then let Sir Palomides and Sir Safere come in after us. But if we should be taken by the people of the castle, then may they rescue us.'

'Lady,' said Sir Dinadan, 'I see that ye are of good courage, and I may not refuse your behest.'

So Igraine the Fair and Sir Dinadan went into the castle, and they found it well furnished at all points, yet no people did they find. And in the hall was a rich banquet set for four persons, and in four chambers were four beds, as though their coming was known.

'This is a strange thing,' said Sir Dinadan, 'and this castle likes me not. For never did I see a feast that set itself, and I fear some trap.'

'I fear nothing,' said Igraine, 'since Sir Palomides is with us. For so much hath he done for me that I deem no hazard could overcome him.'

'Lady,' said Sir Dinadan, 'Sir Palomides is a passing good knight, and I perceive that ye love him well; but what know ye of him? Doth he return your love?'

'As for that,' said Igraine, 'I know not. But in truth I wis he doth not love me overmuch. Yet if he doth not drive me away I am content.'

'Lady,' said Sir Dinadan, 'for what cause brought ye me with you within the castle and not Sir Palomides? Was it to learn of Sir Palomides that ye so did?'

'Yea, I confess it,' said Igraine, 'for I love him more than anything in the world, and ever shall do, good or ill betide. And as for you, Sir Dinadan, well I know that ye will speak that is true and hide nothing from me.'

'Ye put upon me a hard task,' said Sir Dinadan, 'for what man knoweth the truth of another man. Nevertheless I will speak as true as I may, since ye so command me. That Sir

Palomides is a good knight of his hands and a gentle, ye know. And that he is a pagan still, though a christian in his heart ye know also. But he hath cast his love upon La Beale Iseult the queen of Cornwall, that loveth Sir Tristram. And no good will he get of his love, for Sir Tristram is a mightier knight than he and, were Sir Tristram dead, yet would Iseult have none of him. Yet he will not leave his love of her.'

'Of that I had heard report,' said Igraine, 'and, though it grieves me sore, yet I hold it noblesse in Sir Palomides that he is constant in his love without hope.'

'Nay,' said Sir Dinadan, 'thus far he is not constant. For he hath a quest also; and when he is upon his quest for a little time Iseult is not in his mind; and again he bethinketh him of Iseult and forgetteth his quest.'

'The Questing Beast,' said Igraine, 'was the first tidings I had of him. Methinks he must attain that ere I or any other maid have any hope of him.'

'That is also my advice,' said Sir Dinadan, 'and God speed you. For if so be he attain his quest, which needeth strong travail and endurance, then perchance he may turn his thoughts to one that I perceive hath greater constancy than he.'

With that came Sir Palomides and Sir Safere, and they marvelled greatly to find the feast and the chambers all made ready and no man at hand to be seen. So then they sat them down and did eat and drink their fill and had right good cheer. And when they had made an end, Lo! all the platters and the cups and all that was left vanished from their sight. And as they sat astonied, they saw written in letters of gold upon the table these words: 'Now take your rest and fear not. For this is the Castle of Dreams. And one must watch, and three shall dream according to their deserts.'

'Then I will watch,' said Igraine, 'for who knows but on the morrow ye three knights may have sore travail and adventure. But, as for me, I wis I may have many days to rest.'

So then they went to the chambers and Sir Safere, Sir Dinadan and Sir Palomides laid them down to sleep. And the damsel Igraine laid her down but slept not. And in a little while she was ware of the dream of Sir Safere. And he dreamt of tournaments and high adventure and of succouring maidens in distress. And Igraine arose and went to the door of his chamber, and cried aloud: 'Arise, Sir Safere, and go upon thy way, for high deeds call thee!'

And Sir Safere arose like one still in his dream, and armed him and took his horse, and so passed out of the castle, and saw not Igraine.

Then was she ware of the dream of Sir Dinadan. And he dreamed of a fair land, where men sowed and reaped and were in accord with their neighbours. And none made jousts nor tournaments nor battles save when the king summoned his army to defend his land against a foreign foe. So Igraine went to the door of Sir Dinadan's chamber, and called him softly and said:

'Alas, Sir Dinadan, good knight, that dreamest of things that shall not be yet nor in your life time! Arise, then, and go thy way ere thy dream overwhelm thee so that thy life may not be endured!'

Then Sir Dinadan arose and took his armour, and he came to the lady Igraine, and kissed her, and said:

'It was a fair dream, but ye did right to wake me. For a man must live in the world as it is, and amend it a little if he may. And now I pray God for you, Lady, that your waiting may not be overlong.'

So when Sir Dinadan was departed, Igraine was ware of Sir Palomides' dream. And she went to the chamber and looked long upon him as he lay sleeping. And she was sore troubled, for his dream was all a confusion and he tossed and turned in his sleep. And the dream was now of Queen Iseult and now of the Questing Beast and now of his mother, the Lady Etain, and once of Igraine; and then again of Iseult. And so it ranged hither and thither while Sir Palomides moaned in his sleep.

Then Igraine the Fair kneeled adown upon her knees there within the chamber, and prayed to the Lord Jesu Christ that he would send order into the dream, and above all that Sir Palomides would dream more steadfastly of the Questing Beast. And a little she prayed for herself also. And the Lord heard her prayer, and in a little Queen Iseult faded from the dream, and Sir Palomides dreamed of the Beast and of his quest. And then he dreamed of Igraine and of his mother together.

And with that Sir Palomides awoke and saw Igraine the Fair as she knelt in prayer within his chamber. And well he knew that her prayer was for him. Then Sir Palomides spake softly to her and said:

'Lady Igraine, very patient hast thou been with me that have taken you far from your country. But greater patience must I ask of you yet. For I am a knight errant that have a quest and too long have I left it. And now, if ye be willing, I will take you to my mother, the Lady Etain, and there ye may abide.'

'Be it as ye say,' said Igraine, 'for whatsoever ye ordain I am content therewith.'

'Then let us call my brother and Sir Dinadan,' said Sir Palomides, 'so that we may depart hence.'

'They two be gone already,' said Igraine, 'for each of them dreamed a dream, and was in haste to pursue it.'

So Sir Palomides and the Lady Igraine took their horses and rode from the Castle of Dreams. But Igraine hid the dreams of the three knights in her heart and spake not of them. And on a day they came to the castle of the Lady Etain, and right glad was she to see her dear son. And then Sir Palomides requested of her to keep Igraine with her as though she were her own daughter.

So there they abode for three days, and ever the Lady Etain watched covertly and saw the love of Igraine for Sir Palomides. And the Lady Etain was sad at heart that he did not at that time return her love, though he was passing gentle to her. And on the fourth day Sir Palomides took leave of his mother and of Igraine the Fair and departed on his quest. And the Lady Etain cherished Igraine and spake her fair and bade her be strong in love and hope whatever might betide.

XIII

The Castle of Joyous Garde

Now after that King Mark and Queen Iseult and Sir Tristram were come into Cornwall, then on a day by treachery King Mark made Sir Tristram to be cast into prison. And then Queen Iseult rescued Sir Tristram from the prison. But in Cornwall might they not stay. So they came to Logres unto Sir Lancelot. And Sir Lancelot bade them welcome and made them to be housed in Joyous Garde.

Now on a day whilst Sir Tristram and La Beale Iseult were at Joyous Garde, Sir Tristram rode a-hunting and passed by a fair well. And then Sir Tristram alit and put off his helm to drink of that burbly well; and right so he heard the Questing Beast coming toward the well. So when Sir Tristram heard that beast he put on his helm, for he deemed he should hear of Sir Palomides. Right so Sir Tristram saw where came a knight armed upon a noble courser, and so he saluted him.

So they spoke of many things, and this knight's name was Sir Breuse-sans-Pité. Right so came the Questing Beast to the well and drank; but when she saw the knights so nigh her she ran off so fast as though the fiend pursued her. And with that came Sir Palomides, and either saluted other. And he demanded of them whither the Beast had gone.

'Who art thou,' said Sir Breuse, 'that askest?'

'A knight errant that journey upon mine own business.'

Then Tristram knew this was Sir Palomides and said to

him that they two would fain pursue the Beast, for he would hear what he would say.

'Nay,' said Sir Palomides, 'for I will have no companion on my quest, save he overcome me in fair fight.'

At that Sir Breuse laughed and said:

'Take care, ye that will have no companions, that ye fall not into the misfortunes of King Mark of Cornwall, that would no companion for his wife. For now has he lost honour, liberty, and land. La Beale Iseult hath delivered Sir Tristram from prison and went cleanly away with him into this land. And now, sirs, wit you well that King Mark is put in prison by his own knights, and all was for love of Sir Tristram.'

'An this be truth,' said Sir Palomides, 'we shall hear hastily of Sir Tristram. And as for me I dare make good that I do love La Beale Iseult, and that she hath my service above all other ladies and shall have all the term of my life.'

And right so as he spake, they saw before them where came a knight all armed on a great horse, and his one man bore his shield and the other his spear. And anon as that knight espied them he gat his shield and his spear, and dressed him to joust.

'Now, fair fellows,' said Sir Tristram, 'yonder is a knight will joust with us. Now let us see which of us shall encounter with him, for I see well he is of the court of King Arthur.'

'It shall not be long ere he be met withal,' said Sir Palomides, 'for I find never no knight in my quest of this glatising Beast but, an he would joust, I never yet refused him.'

So Sir Palomides dressed him unto that other knight. And so they met so hard that Sir Palomides fell to the earth, horse and man. Then that knight saw Sir Breuse, and cried aloud:

'Make ready, thou false traitor knight, Sir Breuse-sans-Pité!

For I will have ado with thee to the outrance[1] for the noble knights and ladies thou hast betrayed!'

When Sir Breuse heard him say so, he took his horse by the bridle and fled his way as fast as ever his horse might run. When the knight saw him flee he followed fast after through thick and through thin. And as Sir Breuse fled, he saw even afore him three knights of the Table Round; that one hight Sir Ector de Maris and the other hight Sir Percival de Galis and the third hight Sir Harry de Fise Lake. So when Sir Breuse saw these knights he rode straight unto them and prayed them of rescue and cried:

'Ah fair knights, here followeth me the most traitor knight and the most coward and the most of villainy, and his name is Sir Breuse-sans-Pité. And if he may get me he will slay me without mercy and pity.'

And anon they were ware of the knight that came after and they put them forth to joust. And first that knight smote down Sir Ector and after him Sir Percival. And thereafter he and Sir Harry met together so strongly that both the horses and the knights fell to the earth.

And then as the knight uprose and his horse began to recover Sir Breuse came hurtling and smote him over and over, and would have slain him as he lay on the ground. Then Sir Harry arose lightly and took the bridle of Sir Breuse horse and said:

'Fie for shame! Strike never a knight when he is at the earth! For this knight may be called no shameful knight of his deeds, for on this ground he hath done worshipfully and put to the worse passing good knights.'

And as Sir Harry would have taken his horse to fight with

[1] end, death.

Sir Breuse, then Sir Breuse ran upon him as he was half upon his horse, and smote him down, horse and man, and had near slain Sir Harry, the good knight. And by that Sir Percival was upon his horse and rode against Sir Breuse, crying: 'Traitor knight, what dost thou?'

Then Sir Breuse fled all that ever he might, and Sir Percival and Sir Harry followed him fast; but ever the longer they chased the further were they behind. Then they turned again and came to Sir Ector de Maris and that other knight. And the knight said:

'Why have ye so succoured that false traitor knight, Sir Breuse? He is the most coward knight and a devourer of ladies, and also a destroyer of King Arthur's knights as great as any is now living.'

'Alas, Sir,' said Sir Ector, 'then who art thou?'

'My name is,' he said, 'Sir Bleoberis de Ganis.'

'Alas, fair cousin,' said Sir Ector, 'forgive me, for I am Sir Ector de Maris.'

Then all they made great joy of other, but all they were heavy that Sir Breuse-sans-Pité had escaped them, whereof they made great dole.

Now Sir Tristram, when Sir Bleoberis had sped after Sir Breuse, sounded his horn to call in his hunting dogs, and so went to the castle of Joyous Garde. But Sir Palomides took his horse and rode after Sir Bleoberis that yet he knew not. And anon he came upon the four knights as they talked together; and when he saw the shield of Sir Bleoberis lie on the earth, he said:

'He that owneth that shield let him dress him to me, for he smote me down here fast by at a fountain, and therefore I will fight with him on foot.'

'Sir, I am ready,' said Sir Bleoberis, 'here to answer thee, for wit thou well, sir knight, it was I, and my name is Sir Bleoberis de Ganis.'

'Well art thou met,' said Sir Palomides, 'and wit thou well my name is Sir Palomides the Saracen.'

'Sir Palomides,' said Sir Ector, 'wit thou well there is neither thou nor no other knight that beareth the life that slayeth any of our blood but he shall die for it. Therefore, an thou list to fight go and seek Sir Lancelot or else Sir Tristram, and there shalt thou find thy match.'

'With them have I met', said Sir Palomides, 'but I had never no worship of them.'

'Was there never no manner of knight,' said Sir Ector, 'but they two that ever matched you?'

'Yes,' said Sir Palomides, 'there was the third; as good a knight as any of them, and of his age he was the best, for yet found I never his peer. For an he might have lived till he had been more of age, an hardier man there liveth not than he would have been, and his name was Sir Lamorak de Galis. And as he had jousted at a tournament there he overthrew me and thirty knights more, and there he won the prize. And at his departure there met him Sir Gawaine and his brethren, and with great pain they slew him feloniously, unto all good knights' great damage.'

And anon as Sir Percival heard that his brother was dead, he fell over his horse's mane swooning, and there he made the greatest dole and sorrow that ever made any noble knight. And when Sir Percival arose, he said:

'Alas, my good and noble brother, Sir Lamorak, now shall we never meet! And I trow in all the world may not a man find such a knight as he was of his age. And it is much to suffer the death of our father, King Pellinore, and now the death of our good brother, Sir Lamorak.'

Now in this meanwhile there came a varlet from the Court of King Arthur and told them of the great tournament that should be at Lonazep. And so Sir Bleoberis and Sir Palomides were accorded for that time, and Sir Palomides departed from them.

And as Sir Palomides journeyed, he came to Joyous Garde where Sir Tristram was and La Beale Iseult with him, and there he lodged secretly. And Sir Guidaban, son to a lord of those parts, was smitten with love for Queen Iseult, and he took his brother, and they two waited by a way that Sir Tristram would pass, for that they would fall upon him suddenly, and take Queen Iseult from him!

And it chanced that Sir Palomides passed that way, and to him the brethren told their plan. And Sir Palomides was wroth and challenged them to battle, and anon came La Beale Iseult and Sir Tristram. And Sir Palomides, when he saw La Beale Iseult, redoubled his blows, and Guidaban he slew and sore wounded his brother. Then Sir Palomides rode to Sir Tristram and bade him yield Queen Iseult. And then they ran together, and Sir Tristram smote Sir Palomides to the earth.

And Sir Tristram said to Queen Iseult: 'What will ye that I do to Sir Palomides? Shall he live or die?'

'Do what thou wilt,' said she, 'for I care not.'

Then said Sir Tristram:

'A right valiant knight is this Sir Palomides, and of a stout heart. For scarce had he finished a sore battle against odds, wherein he suffered many grievous wounds, when he did battle with me that am fresh and unharmed. Worthy indeed is he to live.'

And so Sir Tristram and La Beale Iseult passed on their way. But Sir Palomides was passing heavy, and rode again upon his way towards Lonazep. And soon thereafter there overtook him Sir Tristram, Sir Dinadan and Sir Gareth and so all they four rode together towards the coast of Lonazep.

So thus they rode until they came to Humber bank, where they heard a cry and a doleful noise. Then were they ware where came sailing a rich vessel covered with red silk, and the vessel came to land close by them. Therewith Sir Tristram alit and went into the vessel. And when he came in, he saw a fair bed richly covered and thereon lay a seemly dead knight, all armed save the head, all bloody with deadly wounds upon him, and a letter in his hand.

'Now, master mariners,' said Sir Tristram, 'how came this knight by his death, and what meaneth this letter?'

'Sir,' said they, 'by that letter shall ye hear and know how he was slain.'

And therewithal Sir Tristram took the letter out of the knight's hand and opened it and read it: and thus it specified:

'Hermance, King and Lord of the Red City, I send to all noble knights of Arthur's court, beseeching them all among them to find one knight that will fight for my sake with two brethren that I brought up out of nought: and feloniously and traitorly they slew me. Wherefore I beseech one good knight to revenge my death; and he that so doeth I will that he have my Red City and all my castles.'

'So God me help,' said Sir Tristram, 'here is a piteous case. And full fain I would take this enterprise; but I have made such a promise that needs I must be at this great jousts and tournament, or else I am shamed. For well I wot for my sake in especial my Lord King Arthur made this jousts in this country, and many worshipful people will be here for to see me. And therefore I fear to take this enterprise upon me lest I come not again betimes to this jousts.'

'Sir,' said Sir Palomides, 'I pray you give me this enterprise. And ye shall see me achieve it worshipfully or else I shall die in this quarrel.'

'Well,' said Sir Tristram, 'this enterprise I give you.'

So departed Sir Tristram, Sir Gareth, and Sir Dinadan and so left Sir Palomides in the vessel. And when he was aboard, the mariners sailed the vessel down the Humber.

XIV

The Delectable Isle

THEN the vessel came to the sea coast, and thereby was a fair castle. And at that time it was early in the morning, afore day. Then the mariners went unto Sir Palomides, that slept fast.

'Sir knight,' said they, 'ye must arise, for here is a castle ye must go into.'

And therewithal Sir Palomides arose and went to the castle, and then he blew his horn that the mariners had given him. And when they in the castle heard that horn, they stood upon the walls and said with one voice: 'Welcome be ye to this castle.'

And then it waxed clear day, and Sir Palomides entered into the castle. And within a while he was served with many divers meats. Then Sir Palomides heard about him much weeping and great dole.

'What may this mean?' said Sir Palomides. 'For I love not to hear such a sorrowful noise.'

Then there came before him a knight that hight Sir Ebell and said thus:

'Wit you well, sir knight, this dole and sorrow is made here every day, and for this cause. We had a king that hight Hermance, and he was king of the Red City. And this king was a noble knight large, and liberal of his expenses. And in all the world he loved nothing so much as he did errant knights of King Arthur's court, and all jousting, hunting and all manner of knightly games: for so good a king and knight had never the rule of poor people. And because of his goodness and gentle ways we bemoan him, and ever shall. And all kings and estates may beware by our lord; for he was destroyed in his own default. For had he cherished his own blood, he had been a live king and lived with great riches and rest. But alas that we should give all others warnings by his death!'

'Tell me,' said Sir Palomides, 'how and in what manner was your lord slain, and by whom.'

'Sir,' said Sir Ebell, 'our king brought up of children two men that now are perilous knights: and these two knights he had them so in favour that he loved no man nor trusted no man of his own blood nor none other that was about him. And by these two knights our king was governed; and so they ruled him easily and his lands, and never would they suffer none of his blood to have no rule with our king. And that espied the lords of our king's blood and departed from him unto their own livelihood.

'And, when these traitors understood that they had driven all the lords of his blood from him, then were they not pleased with such rule but ever thought to have more. And, as ever, it is an old saw—"Give a devil rule and thereby he will not be sufficed"; for whatsoever he be that is ruled by a villain born and the lord of the land is a gentleman born, that same villain shall destroy all the gentlemen about him. And, therefore, sir, an ye be a knight of King Arthur's court, remember this tale, for this is the end and conclusion.

'My lord and king rode into the forest hereby by the advice of these two traitors, and there he chased the red deer, fully armed like a good knight. And so for labour he waxed dry, and then he alit and drank at a well. And, when he was alit by the assent of these two traitors, the one which hight Helyus suddenly smote our king through the body with a spear; and so they left him there. And, when they were departed, there by fortune I came to the well and found my lord and king wounded unto death. And, when I heard his complaint I let bring him to the water's side, and in that same ship I put him on live. And, when my lord King Hermance was in that vessel, he required me for the true faith I owed unto him for to write the letter that ye have seen.

'And this letter I wrote by my Lord's commandment, and then he received his Creator. And he commanded me to put that letter fast in his hand when he was dead or ever he was cold, and to sail forth the vessel up the Humber stream; and to give the mariners commandment never to stint[1] till they came unto Lonazep, where all the noble knights shall assemble at this time. For there he deemed some good knight should have pity of him and revenge his death.

'Now ye know all how our lord was betrayed. And therefore we require you for God's sake have pity upon his death, and worshipfully may ye then rule all his lands. For we all wit well, an ye may slay those two traitors, the Red City and all that be therein will take you for their natural lord.'

'Truly,' said Sir Palomides, 'it grieveth mine heart for to hear you tell this doleful tale. And to say the truth one of the best knights of the world read that letter to me, and by his commandment I came hither to revenge your king's death. And therefore let me wit where I shall find these traitors, for I shall never be at ease in my heart till I be in hands[2] with them '

[1] stop.   [2] at close quarters.

'Sir,' said Sir Ebell, 'then take your ship again. For that ship must bring you unto the Delectable Isle fast by the Red City. And we in this castle shall pray for you and abide your again-coming. For this same castle, an ye speed well, must needs be yours. For our king, Hermance, let make this castle for the love of those two traitors; and so we kept it with strong hand, and therefore full sore are we threatened.'

'Wot ye what ye shall do,' said Sir Palomides. 'What-somever come of me, look ye keep well this castle. For, an it misfortune me to be slain in this quest, I am sure there will come one of the best knights of the world for to revenge my death; and that is Sir Tristram of Lyones or else Sir Lancelot du Lake.'

Then Sir Palomides departed from that castle. And so he came unto the ship, and sailed to the Delectable Isle. Then all they in the Red City made great joy, and sent unto the two brethren at a castle there beside, and bade them make ready, for there was a knight come of King Arthur's to fight with them both at once.

'He is welcome,' said they, 'but is it Sir Lancelot or any of his blood?'

'Nay, Sirs,' said the messenger. 'His name is Sir Palomides, that is yet unchristened, a noble knight.'

'Then we care the less,' said they. 'And, an he be now unchristened, he shall never be christened.'

So they appointed to be at the city within two days. And all the people praised Sir Palomides, and thought him well-made and cleanly and bigly and unmaimed of his limbs, and neither too young nor too old.

And though he were not christened, yet he believed in the best manner, and was full faithful and true of his promise, and well-conditioned.[1] But he had made his avow that he would never be christened unto the time that he achieved the Beast Glatisant, the which was a full wonderful beast and a great signification: for Merlin prophesied much of that beast. And also Sir Palomides avowed never to take full Christendom until he had done seven battles within lists.

So within the third day there came to the city these two brethren, Helyus and Helake; and howbeit that they were false and full of treason, and but poor men born, yet were they noble knights of their hands. And with them they brought forty knights to the intent that they should be big enough for the Red City. Thus came the two brethren with great bobbance[2] and pride.

So when they were all come into the lists, the two brethren came against Sir Palomides together, and he against them, as fast as their horses might run. And Sir Palomides smote Sir Helake through his shield and through his breast more than a fathom. And therewith Sir Helyus, that had kept a little off, came hurtling unto Sir Palomides, ere he could recover his spear, and smote him quite from his horse. So Sir Helyus rode over Sir Palomides twice or thrice. And therewith Sir Palomides was ashamed, and gat the horse of Sir Helyus by the bridle. And therewithal the horse reared, and Sir Palomides pulled him backward, and so horse and man fell to the earth.

Anon Sir Helyus started up lightly, and there he smote Sir Palomides a great stroke upon the helm that he kneeled upon his knee. And then they lashed together many sad strokes, and traced and traversed now backward now sidelong, hurtling together like two boars, and at the same time they both fell grovelling to the earth.

[1] full of good qualities.   [2] boasting.

Thus they fought still without any reposing two hours and never took breath. And then Sir Palomides waxed faint and weary; and Sir Helyus waxed passing strong and doubled his strokes, and drove Sir Palomides overthwart and endlong[1] all the field.

Then when they of the city saw Sir Palomides in this case they made great dole, saying: 'Alas that this noble knight should thus be slain for our King's sake.'

And, as they were thus weeping and crying, at last Sir Palomides, which had suffered an hundred strokes that wonder it was that he stood on his feet, looked about as he might weakly unto the common people how they wept for him. And then he said to himself: 'Fie for shame, Palomides! Why hang ye your head so low?'

And therewith he bare up his shield and looked Sir Helyus in the vizor, and smote him a great stroke upon the helm, and after that another and another. And then he smote Sir Helyus with such a might that he felled him to the earth grovelling. And then he raced off his helm from his head, and so smote off his head from the body.

Then were the people of the city the merriest people that might be. So they brought him to his lodging with great solemnity, and there all the people became his men. And then Sir Palomides prayed them to take keep unto all the lordship of King Hermance.

'For, fair sirs, wit ye well I may not as at this time abide with you, for I must in all haste be with my lord, King Arthur, at the castle of Lonazep.'

Then were the people full heavy at his departing, for all the city proffered him the third part of their goods so that he

[1] across and along, i.e. all over.

would abide with them, but he would not. And so he departed, and came unto the castle where Sir Ebell was lieutenant. And when they in the castle wist how he had sped there was great joy.

And so Sir Palomides departed and came to the castle of Lonazep. Now Sir Tristram had commanded that what knight errant should come within the town that they should warn Sir Tristram. So there came a man of the town and told Sir Tristram how there was a knight in the town, a passing goodly man. And when the man had told the signs of him Sir Dinadan deemed it was Sir Palomides. And then Sir Dinadan went into the town and there found him, and either made other great cheer, and so they lay together that night. And in the morn came Sir Tristram and Sir Gareth and took them in their beds: and so they arose and brake their fast.

And then Sir Tristram dressed[1] Sir Palomides unto the fields and woods, and so they were accorded to repose them in the forest. And when they had played them a great while, they returned to the castle.

Then Sir Tristram asked Sir Palomides of his battle, and how that he had sped at the Red City. And when he heard all, Sir Tristram praised Sir Palomides, for that he had done worshipfully.

Then Sir Tristram devised to send his two pavilions on the morn to set them fast by the well of Lonazep; and therein should be Queen Iseult.

But when Sir Palomides heard that, his heart was ravished out of measure; notwithstanding, he said but little. So Sir Palomides would not have gone into the castle, but Sir Tristram had him by the hand. And when Sir Palomides

[1] led.

5 King Arthur and Sir Lancelot go to see Queen Iseult (with Sir Tristram, Sir Dinadan and Sir Palomides *(see page* 137)

6 Sir Tristram and Sir Lancelot hunting at Joyous Garde *(see page* 166)

saw La Beale Iseult he was so ravished that he might unnethe[1] speak. So they went unto meat: but Sir Palomides might not eat though there was all the cheer that might be had. And so on the morn they were apparelled for to ride unto the field.

[1] hardly.

E

XV

The Tournament at Lonazep

SIR TRISTRAM had three squires and Queen Iseult had three gentlewomen, and both the queen and they were richly apparelled. And other people had they none with them but varlets to bear their shields and their spears. And thus they rode forth. And as they rode they saw afore them a rout of knights; and that was Sir Galihodin with twenty knights with him.

'Now, fair fellows,' said Sir Galihodin, 'yonder come four knights, and a rich and a well fair lady; and I am in will to take that fair lady from them.'

'Sir, that is not best,' said one of them, 'but send ye to them and await what they will say.'

And so they did, and anon there came a squire unto Sir Tristram, and asked him whether they would joust; or else to lose that lady.

'Not so,' said Sir Tristram, 'but tell your lord and bid him come as many as we be and win her and take her.'

'Sir,' said Sir Palomides, 'an it please you, let me have this deed; and I shall undertake them all four.'

'Sir, I will that ye have it,' said Sir Tristram, 'at your pleasure.'

So the squire departed and told Sir Galihodin. Then he dressed his shield and put forth a spear, and Sir Palomides smote Sir Galihodin so hard that horse and man both yode[1]

---

[1] went.

to the earth, and then he had an horrible fall. And then came a second knight, and the same wise he served him: and so he served the third and fourth that he smote them over their horses' cruppers. And always Sir Palomides' spear was whole.

'Ah, Sir Palomides,' said Sir Tristram, 'right well have ye done and worshipfully, as a good knight should.'

Now this Sir Galihodin was nigh kin unto Sir Galahalt the Haut Prince; and this Sir Galihodin was a king within the country of Surluse. And so they passed on their way.

And as they rode they saw afore them four knights and every knight had a spear in his hand. The first was Sir Gawaine, the second was Sir Uwaine, the third was Sir Sagramore le Desirous, and the fourth was Sir Dodinas le Savage. And when Sir Palomides beheld them, that the four knights were ready to joust, he prayed Sir Tristram to give him leave to have ado with them so long as he might hold him on horseback. And all those four Sir Palomides smote down with divers spears.

So when Sir Tristram and his company had departed there came thither Sir Galihodin and his twenty knights unto Sir Gawaine, and there he told them all how he had sped.

'By my troth,' said Sir Gawaine, 'I marvel what knights they be that are so arrayed all in green.'

'And that knight upon the white horse smote me down,' said Sir Galihodin, 'and three of my fellows.'

'So did he me,' said Sir Gawaine, 'and my three fellows. And well I wot that he upon the white horse is Sir Tristram or else Sir Palomides, and that well-beseen[1] lady is Queen Iseult.'

In the meantime Sir Tristram came to the well where his pavilions were set, and there they alighted. And there they

[1] good-looking.

saw many pavilions and great array. And Sir Tristram left there Sir Palomides and Sir Gareth with La Beale Iseult, and Sir Tristram and Sir Dinadan rode unto Lonazep to hearken tidings; and Sir Tristram rode upon Sir Palomides' white horse. And there he learned that King Arthur would be upon the one one side; and upon the other the King of Ireland, and the King of Surluse, and the Kings of Listenoise and of Northumberland and of the best part of Wales. And therewithal he returned and went unto his pavilion.

And by advice of Sir Palomides they agreed together that on the morn they would be of the party against King Arthur for so might they win more worship. And when it was day they were arrayed all in green trappings, both shields and spears, and La Beale Iseult in the same colour, and her three damsels. So the four knights came into the field and passed through from end to end, and so they led Queen Iseult thither where she should stand and behold all the jousts in a bay window. But always she was wimpled that no man might see her visage. And then the four knights rode straight unto the party of the King of Scots.

When King Arthur had seen them do all this, he asked Sir Lancelot what were these knights and this lady.

'Sir,' said Sir Lancelot, 'I cannot tell you for no certain. But if Sir Tristram be in this country or Sir Palomides, wit you well it be they; and there is Queen Iseult.'

Then King Arthur called unto him Sir Kay, and said: 'Go ye lightly and wit how many knights there be here lacking of the Table Round, for by the sieges[1] ye may know.'

So went Sir Kay and saw by the writing in the sieges that there lacked ten knights, and these were their names: Sir

[1] seats.

Tristram, Sir Palomides, Sir Percival, Sir Gareth, Sir Gaheris, Sir Epinogris, Sir Mordred, Sir Dinadan, Sir Brunor that was nicknamed La Cote mal Taille, and Sir Pelleas, the noble knight.

'Well,' said King Arthur, 'some of these, I dare undertake, are here this day against us.'

Then came therein two brethren, cousins unto Sir Gawaine, the one hight Sir Edward and the other Sir Sadok, and asked of King Arthur that they might have the first jousts. So then Sir Edward encountered with the King of Scots and gave him a great fall, and likewise Sir Sadok smote the King of North Wales down. And there was a great cry on King Arthur's party.

That made Sir Palomides passingly wroth, and so he dressed his shield and his spear; and with all his might he met with Sir Edward and smote him so hard that his horse had no might to stand on his feet, and so he hurled down to earth. And then with the same spear Sir Palomides smote down Sir Sadok over his horse's crupper.

'Ah Jesu!' said King Arthur, 'What knight is that arrayed so all in green? For he jousteth mightily.'

'Wit you well,' said Sir Gawaine, 'he is a good knight, and yet shall we see him joust better or he depart. And yet shall ye see a more bigger knight in the same colour than he is. For that same knight, that smote down right now my two cousins, smote me down within these two days, and seven fellows more.'

Then as they stood talking, there came into the place Sir Tristram upon a black horse. And or ever he stayed he smote down with one spear four good knights of Orkney, and Sir Gareth and Sir Dinadan every each of them smote down a good knight.

'Ah Jesu!' said Arthur, 'Yonder knight upon the black horse doth mightily and marvellously well.'

'Abide you!' said Sir Gawaine, 'That knight on the black horse began not yet.'

Then Sir Tristram and Sir Palomides rode unto the thickest press against them of Orkney, and smote down knights, and so fared that King Arthur and all knights had great marvel. And King Arthur likened Sir Tristram that was on the black horse, unto a wood lion; and he likened Sir Palomides upon the white horse to a wood leopard, and Sir Gareth and Sir Dinadan unto eager wolves. And they of Orkney waxed weary and so withdrew them into Lonazep.

Then the heralds numbered that Sir Tristram had smitten down thirty knights, and Sir Palomides twenty knights.

'So God me help,' said King Arthur unto Sir Lancelot, 'this is a great shame to see four knights beat so many knights of mine. And therefore make you ready, for we will have ado with them.'

'Sir,' said Sir Lancelot, 'wit you well that there are two passing good knights, and great worship were it not for us now to have ado with them, for they are greatly travailed.'

'As for that,' said King Arthur, 'I will be avenged. And therefore take with you Sir Bleoberis and Sir Ector de Maris, and I will be the fourth.'

'Well, sir,' said Sir Lancelot, 'ye shall find me ready, and my brother, Sir Ector, and my cousin, Sir Bleoberis.'

And it was agreed that Sir Lancelot should encounter with the knight upon the black horse, and Sir Bleoberis with the knight upon the white horse, and Sir Ector with the knight upon the dun horse, that was Sir Gareth, and King Arthur with the knight upon the grey horse, that was Sir Dinadan.

So then encountered Sir Lancelot against Sir Tristram, and they smote either other so sore that horse and man yode to the earth. But Sir Lancelot weened that it had been Sir Palomides, and so he rose and passed out from the battle. And Sir Bleoberis smote Sir Palomides so hard upon his shield that he and his white horse rosteled[1] to the earth. Then Sir Ector smote Sir Gareth so hard that down he fell from his horse. And King Arthur smote down Sir Dinadan. And then the noise turned awhile, and said: 'The green knights were felled down!'

When the King of Northgalis saw that Sir Tristram was on foot, then he made ready many knights for succour. For the custom and the cry was such that what knight were smitten down and might not be horsed again by his fellows or by his own strength, that as that day he should be prisoner unto the party that smote him down.

So then came in the king of Northgalis and rode straight to Sir Tristram, and alit deliverly, and took him his horse, and said:

'Noble knight, I know thee not nor of what country ye be. But for the noble deeds that ye have done this day take there my horse and let me do as well as I may. For, as Jesu be my help, ye are better worthy to have mine horse than myself.'

'Gramercy!' said Sir Tristram, 'And, if I may, I will quit you. And look that ye go not far from us, and as I suppose I shall win you soon another horse.'

And therewithal Sir Tristram mounted on his horse, and anon he met with King Arthur; and he gave him such a buffet that King Arthur had no power to keep his saddle.

[1] tumbled.

And then Sir Tristram gave the King of Northgalis King Arthur's horse.

Then was there great press about King Arthur for to horse him again. But Sir Palomides would not suffer King Arthur to be horsed again. For ever Sir Palomides on foot smote on the right and on the left hand, and raced off helms mightily as a noble knight.

And so meanwhile Sir Tristram rode through the thickest of the press and so passed forth unto his pavilions. And there he changed his horse, and disguised himself all in red, horse and harness.

Now when Queen Iseult saw Sir Tristram unhorsed and she wist not where he was become, then she wept heartily. But Sir Tristram, when he was ready, came dashing lightly into the field, and then La Beale Iseult espied him. And Sir Lancelot espied him also that it was Sir Tristram, and then he repented him that he had smitten him down.

And when Sir Tristram was come into the press, through his great force he put Sir Palomides upon his horse, and Sir Gareth and Sir Dinadan. But Sir Palomides neither none of his two fellows knew not who had holpen them to horseback.

So when La Beale Iseult espied Sir Tristram again upon horseback, she was passing glad; and then she laughed and made good cheer. And, as it happened, Sir Palomides looked up towards her, as she was in the window, and Sir Palomides espied how she laughed. And therewith he took such rejoicing that he smote down, what with his spear and with his sword, all that ever he met; for through the sight of her he was so enamoured in her love that him seemed at that time that, an both Sir Tristram and Sir Lancelot had been against him, they should have won no worship of him!

So Sir Palomides began to double his strength, and he did so marvellously all men had wonder. And ever he cast up his eyes unto La Beale Iseult. And, when he saw her make such cheer, he fared like a lion, that there might no man withstand him. And then Sir Tristram beheld him how he stirred about, and said unto Sir Dinadan:

'So God me help, Sir Palomides is a passing good knight and a well-enduring: but such deeds saw I him never do, nor never erst heard I tell that ever he did so much in one day.'

'Sir, it is his day,' said Sir Dinadan, and would say no more. But to himself he said: 'An Sir Tristram knew for whose love he doth all these deeds, soon he would abate his courage.'

Then all the people cried for to give Sir Palomides the prize, that that day passed Sir Lancelot and Sir Tristram. Right so came into the field Sir Lancelot, that had long rested him, and saw and heard the great noise and the great worship that Sir Palomides had. Then he dressed him against Sir Palomides with a great spear and a long, and thought to have smitten him down. And Sir Palomides was so wearied that he was nigh out of his mind, and he deemed, when he heard all the noise, that the day was ended.

And so, when he saw Sir Lancelot come upon him so fast, he took his horse with the spurs and ran upon him so fast with his sword. And as Sir Lancelot would have stricken him, he smote the spear aside and smote it in two with his sword. And therewith Sir Palomides thought to put Sir Lancelot to shame, and rushed upon him, and with his sword he smote off his horse's neck that Sir Lancelot rode upon. And then Sir Lancelot fell to earth.

Then was the cry huge and great how Sir Palomides the Saracen had smitten down Sir Lancelot's horse. Right so there were many knights wroth with Sir Palomides because he had done that deed, and held there against it; and said it was unknightly done in a tournament to kill an horse wilfully unless that it had been done in plain battle life for life.

When Sir Ector saw Sir Lancelot have such a despite and so set on foot, then he gat a spear and smote Sir Palomides so hard that he bore him quite from his horse. That saw Sir Tristram, and he smote down Sir Ector. Then Sir Lancelot dressed his shield upon his shoulder and with his sword naked in his hand came straight upon Sir Palomides:

'Wit thou well thou hast done me this day the greatest despite that ever any worshipful knight did me in tournament or in jousts; and therefore I will be avenged upon thee.'

'Ah, mercy, noble knight,' said Sir Palomides, 'of my deeds! Forgive me mine unknightly deeds, for I have no power nor might to withstand you. And I have done so much this day that well I wot I did never so much nor never shall do so much in all my days. And therefore, most noble knight in the world, I require thee spare me this day, and I promise you I shall ever be your knight while I live.'

'Well,' said Sir Lancelot, 'I see, for to say the sooth, ye have done marvellously well this day; and I understand in part for whose love ye did it, and well I wot that love is a great master. And if my lady were here, which she is not, wit you well, Sir Palomides, ye should not bear away the worship. But beware your love be not discovered; for, an Sir Tristram may know it, ye shall repent it. But, since my quarrel is not here, ye shall have this day the worship as for me. Considering the great travail and pain that ye have had this day, it were no worship for me to come against you as I did, nor now to put you from it.'

And then the king let blow to lodging. And because Sir Palomides began first, and never he went nor rode out of the field to repose him but ever he was doing on horseback or on foot and longest enduring, King Arthur and all the kings gave Sir Palomides the honour and the prize for that day.

XVI

More of the Same

THEN Sir Tristram commanded Sir Dinadan to fetch Queen Iseult to his two pavilions by the well. And when Sir Palomides understood and heard that Sir Tristram was he that was in the red armour and on the red horse, wit you well that he was glad; for he weened that Sir Tristram had been taken prisoner. And then they talked together, and Sir Dinadan rallied Sir Tristram and said:

'What the devil is upon this day? For Sir Palomides' strength feebled never this day, but ever he doubled. And Sir Tristram fared all this day as he had been on sleep; and therefore I call him a coward.'

'Well, Sir Dinadan,' said Sir Tristram, 'I was never called coward ere now of earthly knight in my life. And wit thou well I call myself never the more coward though Sir Lancelot gave me a fall, for I outcept[1] him of all knights. And doubt ye not, if Sir Lancelot have a quarrel good, he is too overgood for any knight that now is living: and yet of his sufferance, largesse, bounty, and courtesy I call him a knight peerless.'

And so Sir Tristram was in manner wroth with Sir Dinadan. But all this language Sir Dinadan said because he would anger Sir Tristram for to cause him to wake his spirits: for well knew Sir Dinadan that an Sir Tristram were thoroughly wroth, Sir Palomides should win no worship upon the morn.

[1] except.

'Truly,' said Sir Palomides, 'as for Sir Lancelot, of noble knighthood and of his courtesy, prowess and gentleness, I know not his peer. For this day I did full uncourteously unto Sir Lancelot, and full unknightly. And full knightly and courteously he did to me again: for, an he had been so ungentle to me as I was to him, this day had I won no worship. And therefore I shall be Sir Lancelot's knight whiles that I live.'

So on the morn Sir Tristram was ready, and La Beale Iseult with Sir Palomides and Sir Gareth. And so they rode all in green, full freshly beseen, unto the forest. And Sir Tristram left Sir Dinadan sleeping in his bed. And so as they rode it happened the king and Sir Lancelot stood in a window and saw Sir Tristram ride and La Beale Iseult.

'Take your horse,' said King Arthur, 'and array you at all rights as I will do, and I promise you I will see her.'

And anon they were armed and horsed and either took a spear, and rode into the forest.

'Sir,' said Sir Lancelot, 'I pray you be not too hasty. For peradventure the knights will be displeased an we come suddenly upon them.'

'As for that,' said King Arthur, 'I will see her, for I take no force[1] whom I grieve.'

'Sir,' said Sir Lancelot, 'ye put yourself in great jeopardy.'

'As for that,' said the king, 'we will take the adventure.'

Right so the king rode even to her and said: 'God you save!'

'Sir,' she said, 'ye are welcome.'

Then the king beheld her and liked her wonderly well. But with that came Sir Palomides unto King Arthur and said: 'Thou uncourteous knight, what seekest thou here? For thou

[1] I do not care.

art uncourteous to come upon a lady thus suddenly. Therefore withdraw thee!'

But King Arthur took none heed of Sir Palomides' words, but ever he looked still upon Queen Iseult. Then was Sir Palomides wroth; and therewith he took a spear and came hurtling upon King Arthur and smote him down with the spear a great fall. When Sir Lancelot saw that, he cried to Sir Palomides to keep him well. And therewithal Sir Lancelot and Sir Palomides rushed together with two spears strongly. And Sir Lancelot smote Sir Palomides so hard that he went quite out of his saddle and had a great fall.

When Sir Tristram saw Sir Palomides have that fall, he said to Sir Lancelot: 'Sir knight, keep thee, for I must joust with thee.'

'As for to joust with me,' said Sir Lancelot, 'I will not fail you for no dread that I have of you. But I am loth to have ado with you an I might choose; for I will that ye wit that I must avenge my special lord and my most bedrad[1] friend. And therefore, sir, though I revenge that fall, take ye no displeasure, for he is to me such a friend that I may not see him shamed.'

Anon Sir Tristram understood by his person and his knightly words it was Sir Lancelot du Lake, and truly Sir Tristram deemed that it was King Arthur that Sir Palomides had smitten down. And then Sir Tristram put his spear from him and gat Sir Palomides again on his horse's back; and Sir Lancelot gat King Arthur again to horseback and so departed.

'So God me help,' said Sir Tristram unto Sir Palomides, 'ye did not worshipfully when ye smote down that knight so suddenly as ye did. And wit you well ye did yourself great

[1] revered.

shame; for the knights came hither of their gentleness to see a fair lady, and ye had not ado to play such game for my lady. Wit you well that he that ye smote down was King Arthur, and that other was the good knight, Sir Lancelot. And ever he forbeareth me in every place and showeth me great kindness.'

'Sir, I may never believe,' said Sir Palomides, 'that King Arthur will ride so privily as a poor errant knight.'

'Ah!' said Sir Tristram, 'ye know not my lord, King Arthur, for all knights may learn to be a knight of him. And therefore ye may be sorry of your unknightly deed done to so noble a knight.'

'An a thing, sir, be done, it cannot be undone,' said Sir Palomides.

Then Sir Tristram sent Queen Iseult unto her lodging into the priory, there to behold all the tournament.

Then was there cry unto all knights made that when they heard the horn blow they should make jousts. And when all the knights were come, then came into the place the knights of Orkney, and began to do many deeds of arms. When Sir Tristram saw them so begin, he said to Sir Palomides: 'How feel ye yourself? May ye do this day as ye did yesterday?'

'Nay,' said Sir Palomides, 'I feel myself so weary and so sore bruised of the deeds of yesterday that I may not endure as I did.'

'That me repenteth,' said Sir Tristram, 'for I shall lack you this day.'

'But help yourself,' said Sir Palomides, 'and trust not to me; for I may not do as I did.'

And all these words said Sir Palomides but to beguile Sir Tristram. For he was wroth with Sir Tristram for that he had said on King Arthur's part. Then said Sir Tristram unto Sir Gareth: 'Then must I trust upon you. Wherefore I pray you, be not far from me to rescue me an need be.'

'Sir, I shall not fail you,' said Sir Gareth, 'in all that I may do.'

Then Sir Palomides rode by himself and entered not into the jousts, for indeed he was sore weary. But on a sudden he espied Queen Iseult, and with that he put himself in the thickest press among them of Orkney. And there he did so marvellous deeds of arms that all men had wonder of him, for there might none withstand his strokes. And when Sir Tristram saw Sir Palomides do such deeds, he marvelled and said to himself: 'Methinketh he is weary of my company.'

So Sir Tristram beheld him a great while and did but little else: for the noise and the cry was so great that Sir Tristram marvelled from whence came the strength that Sir Palomides had there.

'Sir,' said Sir Gareth unto Sir Tristram, 'remember ye not of the words that Sir Dinadan said to you yesterday, when he called you coward? Indeed, Sir, he said it for none ill, for ye are the man in the world that he loveth best, and all he said was for your worship. And therefore let me know this day what ye be. And wonder ye not so upon Sir Palomides, for he forceth himself as one that is mad beyond his strength.'

'I may well believe it,' said Sir Tristram.

Then Sir Tristram rode into the thickest of the press. And then he did so marvellously well that all men said that Sir Tristram did double so much deeds of arms as did Sir Palomides aforehand.

'How now?' said Sir Lancelot unto King Arthur, 'I told you that this day there would a knight play his pageant.'

'So God me help,' said King Arthur, 'ye say sooth, for I never saw a better knight; for he passeth far Sir Palomides.'

'Sir, wit you well,' said Sir Lancelot, 'it is himself that noble knight, Sir Tristram.'

But when Sir Palomides heard the noise and the cry was turned from him, he rode out on the town side and beheld Sir Tristram. And when he saw him do so marvellously well, he wept passingly sore for despite, for he wist well that he should win no worship that day. For well knew Sir Palomides, when Sir Tristram would put forth his strength and his manhood, that he should get but little worship that day.

Then came King Arthur and the King of Northgalis and Sir Lancelot du Lake; and Sir Bleoberis and Sir Bors de Ganis and Sir Ector de Maris. And so they did great deeds of arms. But Sir Tristram and Sir Gareth abode still in the field and endured all that ever there came, that all men had wonder that ever any knight endured so many great strokes. But ever Sir Lancelot and his kinsmen forbare Sir Tristram and Sir Gareth.

And on a sudden Sir Tristram rode privily out of the press, that no man espied him but La Beale Iseult and Sir Palomides; for they two would not leave off their eyesight of him. And when Sir Tristram came to his pavilions, he found Sir Dinadan in his bed asleep.

'Awake!' said Sir Tristram, 'for ye ought to be ashamed so to sleep when knights have ado in the field.'

Then Sir Dinadan arose lightly, and said: 'Sir, what will ye do?'

'Make you ready,' said Sir Tristram, 'to ride with me into the field.'

So, when Sir Dinadan was armed, he looked upon Sir

Tristram's helm and on his shield; and when he saw many strokes thereupon, he said:

'In good time was I thus asleep! For, had I been with you, I must needs for shame have followed with you more for shame than for any prowess that is in me. And I see well now by thy strokes that I should have been truly beaten as I was yesterday.'

'Leave your japes,' said Sir Tristram, 'and come off; that we be in the field again.'

And then Sir Tristram arrayed him all in black armour.

'What?' said Sir Dinadan, 'Is your heart up now? Yesterday ye fared as ye had dreamed. But what aileth you this day? Meseemeth that ye be more wilder than ye were yesterday.'

And so they took their horses, and rode to the field.

XVII

The Wrath of Queen Iseult

AND all this espied Sir Palomides both the going and the coming; and so did La Beale Iseult. Then Sir Palomides saw that Sir Tristram was disguised, and thought to shame him. And so he rode unto a knight that was sore wounded, that sat under a thorn a good way from the field.

'Sir knight,' said Sir Palomides, 'I pray you lend me your armour and your shield, for mine is overwell known in this field, and that hath done me great damage. And ye shall have mine armour and my shield that is as sure as yours.'

'I will well,' said the knight, 'that ye have mine armour and also my shield. If they may do you any avail, I am well pleased.'

So Sir Palomides armed him in that knight's armour, and took his shield that shone like any crystal or silver, and so he came riding into the field. And neither Sir Tristram nor none of his party nor of King Arthur's knew Sir Palomides.

And as soon as he came into the field, Sir Tristram smote down three knights, even in the sight of Sir Palomides. And then he rode against Sir Tristram, and either met other with great spears, that they all to-brast in their hands. And then they dashed together with swords eagerly.

Then Sir Tristram had marvel what knight he was that did battle so mightily with him. And Sir Tristram was wroth, for he felt him passing strong: and he deemed that he could not have ado with the remnant of the knights because of the strength of this knight.

So they lashed together and gave many sad strokes; and many knights marvelled what knight he was that so encountered with the black knight. But full well knew La Beale Iseult that it was Sir Palomides, for she espied all in her window whereat she stood, how Sir Palomides changed his harness with the wounded knight. And then she began to weep so heartily for the despite of Sir Palomides that well-nigh there she swooned.

Then came in Sir Lancelot with the knights of Orkney. And there came a knight that prayed him fight with the knight in black armour that had almost overcome the good knight with the silver shield. Then Sir Lancelot rode betwixt them, and said unto Sir Palomides: 'Sir knight, let me have this battle, for ye have need to be reposed.'

Sir Palomides knew well Sir Lancelot, and so did Sir Tristram. But because Sir Lancelot was far hardier knight and bigger than he, Sir Palomides was right glad to suffer Sir Lancelot to fight with Sir Tristram, for he hoped that he should beat or shame Sir Tristram. And so Sir Lancelot, that knew not Sir Tristram, lashed at him many hard strokes. And then they fought long together, which made La Beale Iseult well-nigh out of her mind for sorrow.

Then Sir Dinadan told Sir Gareth how that knight in the black harness was Sir Tristram, and that Sir Lancelot must needs have the better of him, for Sir Tristram had had over-much travail that day.

'Then let us smite him down,' said Sir Gareth.

And so forthwithal Sir Gareth rushed upon Sir Lancelot

and gave him a great stroke upon the helm, that he was astonied. And then came in Sir Dinadan with his spear, and smote Sir Lancelot such a buffet that horse and man yode to earth and had a great fall.

'Now fie for shame!' said Sir Tristram unto Sir Gareth and Sir Dinadan, 'Why did ye so to-smite adown so good a knight as he is, and namely when I had ado with him? Ah Jesu! Ye do yourselves great shame and him no disworship; for I held him reasonably hot, though ye had not holpen me.'

Then came Sir Palomides and smote down Sir Dinadan from his horse. Then Sir Lancelot, because Sir Dinadan had smitten him down aforehand, therefore he assailed Sir Dinadan passing sore. And Sir Dinadan defended him mightily; but well understood Sir Tristram that Sir Dinadan might not endure against Sir Lancelot; wherefore Sir Tristram was sorry.

Then came Sir Palomides fresh upon Sir Tristram. And when he saw him come so freshly, he thought to deliver him at once, because he would help Sir Dinadan that stood in peril with Sir Lancelot. Then Sir Tristram hurtled unto Sir Palomides and gave him a great buffet; and then Sir Tristram gat Sir Palomides and pulled him down underneath his horse's feet. And then Sir Tristram lightly leapt down, and left Sir Palomides, and went betwixt Sir Dinadan and Sir Lancelot: and then they began to do battle together. And right so Sir Dinadan gat Sir Tristram's horse, and said on high, that Sir Lancelot might hear: 'My lord, Sir Tristram, take your horse!'

And when Sir Lancelot heard him name Sir Tristram, he said: 'Ah my lord, Sir Tristram, why come ye now disguised?

I pray you to pardon me, for, an I had known you, we had not done this battle.'

'Sir,' said Sir Tristram, 'this is not the first kindness and goodness ye have shown unto me.'

And anon they were horsed both again. And all the people on the one side gave Sir Lancelot the honour and the prize, and all the people on the other side gave Sir Tristram the honour and the prize. But Sir Lancelot said:

'Nay, for I am not worthy to have this honour. For I will report me to all knights that Sir Tristram hath been longer in the field than I, and he hath smitten down many more knights this day than I have done. And therefore I will give Sir Tristram my voice and my name, and so I pray all my lords and fellows so to do.'

Then there was the whole voice of kings, dukes, and earls, barons, and knights that Sir Tristram of Lyones this day is proved the best knight.

Then they blew unto lodgings. And Queen Iseult was led unto her pavilions. But wit you well she was wroth out of measure with Sir Palomides, for she saw all his treason from the beginning to the ending. And all this while neither Sir Tristram nor Sir Gareth nor Sir Dinadan knew not of it.

So then as all they rode to their pavilions with La Beale Iseult, ever Sir Palomides rode with them in their company, disguised as he was. But when Sir Tristram had espied him that he was the same knight with the shield of silver that held him so hot that day, then said Sir Tristram: 'Sir knight, wit you well here is none that hath need of your fellowship. And therefore I pray you depart from us.'

Then Sir Palomides answered again, as though he had not known Sir Tristram: 'Wit thou well, sir knight, that from this fellowship I will not depart. For one of the best knights of the world commanded me to be in this company; and till that he discharge me of my service, I will not be discharged.'

So by his language Sir Tristram knew that it was Sir Palomides, and said: 'Ah sir, are ye such a knight? Ye have been named wrong! For ye have been called ever a gentle knight; and as this day ye have shewed me great ungentleness, for ye had almost brought me to my death. But as for you I suppose I should have done well enough: but Sir Lancelot with you was overmuch, for I know no knight living but Sir Lancelot is too overgood for him an he will do his utterest.'

'Alas,' said Sir Palomides, 'are ye my Lord, Sir Tristram?'

'Yea, sir, and that know you well enough.'

'By my knighthood,' said Sir Palomides, 'how might I know you until now? For I weened ye had been the King of Ireland, for well I wot that he bear his arms.'

'I bear his arms,' said Sir Tristram, 'and that will I abide by. For I won them once in a field of a full noble knight whose name was Sir Marhalt.'

'Sir,' said Sir Palomides, 'I weened that ye had been turned upon Sir Lancelot's party and that caused me to turn.'

'Ye say well,' said Sir Tristram, 'and so I take you and forgive you.'

So then they rode to their pavilions. And when they were alit, they unarmed them, and washed their faces and their hands and so yode unto meat and were set there at table. But when La Beale Iseult saw Sir Palomides, she changed then her colour: for wrath she might not speak. Anon Sir Tristram espied her countenance and said: 'Madam, for what cause make ye us such cheer? We have been sore travailed all this day.'

'Mine own lord,' said La Beale Iseult, 'for God's sake be ye not displeased with me, for I may none otherwise do. I saw this day how ye were betrayed and nigh brought unto your death. Truly, sir, I saw every deal[1], how and in what wise. And therefore, Sir, how should I suffer in your presence such a felon and traitor as Sir Palomides? For I saw him with mine eyes how he beheld you when ye went out of the field. For ever he hoved still upon his horse till that he saw you come againward. And then forthwithal I saw him ride to the hurt knight, and change his harness with him. And then straight I saw him how he sought you through all the field; and anon as he had found you he encountered with you. Wilfully Sir Palomides did battle with you. And as for him I was not greatly afraid, but I dreaded Sir Lancelot that knew not you.'

'Madam,' said Sir Palomides, 'ye may say what ye will, I may not contrary you; but by my knighthood, I knew not my Lord, Sir Tristram.'

'No force,' said Sir Tristram unto Sir Palomides, 'I will take your excuse, but well I wot ye spared me but a little. But no force![2] All is pardoned as on my part.'

Then La Beale Iseult held down her head and said no more at that time.

And therewithal two knights armed came to the pavilion; and then they alit both, and came in armed at all points.

'Fair knights,' said Sir Tristram, 'if ye would anything with us, ye might have eased your hearts when we were in the field. But, an ye come friendly, I require you do off your helms that I may see you.'

[1] part.   [2] no matter.

And when their helms were off, all they there beheld King Arthur and Sir Lancelot. Then the king and the queen kissed, and Sir Lancelot and Sir Tristram embraced either other in arms, and then there was joy without measure. And at the request of La Beale Iseult the king and Sir Lancelot were unarmed. And then there was merry talking. And thus they talked of many things and of the whole jousts.

'But for what cause,' said King Arthur, 'were ye, Sir Tristram, against us? Ye are a knight of the Table Round, and of right ye should have been with us.'

'Sir,' said Sir Tristram, 'here is Sir Dinadan; and Sir Gareth, your own nephew, caused me to be against you.'

'My lord Arthur,' said Sir Gareth, 'I may well bear the blame, for my back is broad enough. But forsooth it was Sir Tristram's own deed.'

'By God, and that may I repent,' said Sir Dinadan. 'For ere I met Sir Tristram I had some small sense. But since I have been of his company he hath led me into so many follies that I am become a fool. And at the last this unhappy Sir Tristram brought us to this tournament, and many great buffets he hath caused us to have.'

Then the king and Sir Lancelot laughed that scarce they might sit.

'But what knight was that,' said King Arthur, 'that held you so short?'

'Sir,' said Sir Tristram, 'here he sitteth at this table.'

'What?' said the king, 'Was it Sir Palomides?'

'Sir, wit you well that it was he,' said Queen Iseult.

'So God me help,' said King Arthur, 'that was unknightly done of you as of so good a knight. For I have heard many people call you a courteous knight.'

'Sir,' said Sir Palomides, 'I knew not Sir Tristram for he was so disguised.'

'So God help me,' said Sir Lancelot, 'that may well be, for I knew him not myself. But I marvelled why ye turned on our party.'

'Sir, as for that,' said Sir Tristram, 'I have pardoned him. And I would be right loth to leave his fellowship, for I love right well his company.'

And so they left off, and talked of other things. And in the evening, King Arthur and Sir Lancelot departed unto their lodging. But wit you well Sir Palomides had great sorrow at heart; and all that night he had never rest in his bed, but wailed and wept out of measure.

XVIII

The Melancholy of Sir Palomides

So on the morn Sir Tristram, Sir Gareth and Sir Dinadan arose early, and went unto Sir Palomides' chamber; and there they found him fast asleep, for he had all night watched. And it was seen upon his cheeks that he had wept full sore.

'Say ye nothing,' said Sir Tristram, 'for I am sure he hath taken anger and sorrow for the rebuke that I gave him and Queen Iseult.'

Then Sir Tristram let call Sir Palomides and bade him make ready, for it was time to go into the field. And anon they armed them and clothed them all in red, both La Beale Iseult and all the fellowship. And so they led her passing freshly through the field into the priory.

And anon they heard three blasts blow, and every king and knight dressed him to the field. And the first that was ready to joust was Sir Palomides and Sir Kaynes le Straunge, a knight of the Round Table, and so they two encountered together. And Sir Palomides smote Sir Kaynes so hard that he bore him quite over his horse's crupper. And forthwithal Sir Palomides smote down another knight, and brake his spear: and then he pulled out his sword and did wondrous well. And then the noise began greatly upon Sir Palomides.

And then in came Sir Tristram as thunder, and he encountered with Sir Kay le Seneschal, and there he smote him down quite from his horse. And with that same spear he smote down three knights more. And then he pulled out his sword and did marvellously. Then the noise and the cry changed from Sir Palomides and turned unto Sir Tristram; and Sir Palomides was clean forgotten. And then came in Sir Gareth and Sir Dinadan and did right well that day.

Then King Arthur and Sir Lancelot took their horses and dressed them to the field among the thickest of the press. And there Sir Tristram unknowing smote down King Arthur. And then Sir Lancelot would have rescued him: but there were so many upon Sir Lancelot that they pulled him down from his horse.

Then came Sir Ector de Maris, and he bore a spear against Sir Palomides and brast it upon him all to shivers. And then Sir Ector came again and gave Sir Palomides such a dash with a sword that he stooped adown upon his saddle-bow. And forthwithal Sir Ector pulled down Sir Palomides under his horse's feet, and took his horse to Sir Lancelot and bade him mount upon him. But Sir Palomides leapt before and smote Sir Ector aside and gat his horse by the bridle and leapt into the saddle.

'So God me help,' said Sir Lancelot, 'ye are better worthy to have that horse than I.'

Then Sir Ector brought Sir Lancelot another horse, and anon Sir Lancelot gat the king again on horse back. Then King Arthur and Sir Lancelot did marvellous deeds of arms; yet their party was but few and they were overmatched. And when Sir Tristram saw that, he called unto him Sir Palomides, Sir Gareth and Sir Dinadan, and said thus to them:

'My fair fellows, wit you well that I will turn unto King Arthur's party, for I saw never so few men do so well. And it will be shame unto us that be knights of the Round Table to see our Lord, King Arthur, and that noble knight, Sir Lancelot, to be dishonoured.'

'Sir, it will be well done,' said Sir Gareth and Sir Dinadan.

'Sir, do your best,' said Sir Palomides, 'for I will not change my party that I came in withal.'

'That is for envy of me,' said Sir Tristram, 'but God speed you well in your journey!'

And so Sir Palomides departed from them. And Sir Tristram, Sir Gareth and Sir Dinadan turned with Sir Lancelot. And then Sir Lancelot smote down the King of Ireland and two other kings. And King Arthur ran unto Sir Palomides and smote him quite from his horse. And Sir Tristram bore down all that ever he met withal, and Sir Gareth and Sir Dinadan did then as noble knights. And anon all the other party began to flee.

And then Sir Palomides went his way wailing, and so withdrew him till he came to a well. And there he put his horse from him and did off his armour, and wailed and wept like as he had been a wood man.

And when the trumpets blew to lodgings, then many knights gave the prize unto Sir Tristram, and Sir Tristram gave it unto Sir Lancelot, but Sir Lancelot would none of it. And so at the last the prize was given betwixt them both. And so every man rode to his lodging.

Now as Sir Palomides was at the well, there came by the kings of Wales, and of Scotland, and they saw Sir Palomides in that distress.

'Alas,' said they, 'so noble a man as ye be should be in this array!'

And then they gat him his horse again and made him to

arm him and mount upon his horse. And so he rode with them, making great dole. And it chanced that they came nigh to the pavilions of Sir Tristram: and Sir Palomides prayed the two kings to abide him there while that he spake with Sir Tristram. And when he came to the door of the pavilion, Sir Palomides said on high: 'Where art thou, Sir Tristram de Lyones?'

'Sir,' said Sir Dinadan, 'that is Sir Palomides.'

'What, Sir Palomides,' said Sir Tristram, 'will ye not come here among us?'

'Fie on thee, traitor!' said Sir Palomides, 'for wit thou well, an it were daylight as it is night, I should slay thee with mine own hands. And if ever I may get thee, thou shalt die for this day's deed.'

'Sir Palomides,' said Sir Tristram, 'ye blame me wrongly; for, had ye done as I did, ye should have had worship. But sithen ye give me so large warning, I shall be ware of you.'

'Fie on thee, traitor!' said Sir Palomides; and therewithal he departed.

And Sir Palomides rode with the two kings, and ever he made the greatest dole that any man could think. For he was not only so dolorous for the departing from La Beale Iseult, but he was as sorrowful to go from the fellowship of Sir Tristram. For he was so kind and so gentle that when Sir Palomides remembered him he might never be merry.

And on the morn Sir Tristram and La Beale Iseult, Sir Gareth and Sir Dinadan went by land and water to Joyous Garde; and with them went Sir Bleoberis and Sir Ector de Maris. And King Arthur and his knights drew into Camelot. And after a seven night Bleoberis and Sir Ector departed from

Sir Tristram and came thereas Queen Guinevere was lodged in a castle by the seaside. And through the grace of God the queen was recovered from her malady. And when she knew from whence they came, the queen said: 'How doth Sir Tristram and La Beale Iseult?'

'Truly, Madam,' said the knights, 'he doth as a noble knight should do. And as for the queen, she is peerless of all ladies: for to speak of her beauty, bounty and mirth, and of her goodness, we saw never her match as far as we have ridden and gone.'

'Ah mercy Jesu!' said Queen Guinevere, 'thus saith all folks that have seen her and spoken with her. God would that I had part of her conditions! And was now misfortuned me of my sickness while that tournament endured, for, as I suppose, I shall never see in all my life such assembly of noble knights and fair ladies.'

And then the knights told the queen how Sir Palomides won the prize the first day with great noblesse, and the second day Sir Tristram won it, and the third Sir Tristram and Sir Lancelot betwixt them.

'Well,' said Queen Guinevere, 'who did best all three days?'

'So God me help,' said they, 'Sir Lancelot and Sir Tristram had there least dishonour. And wit you well, Sir Palomides did passingly well and mightily. But he turned against the party that he came in withal, and that caused him to lose a great part of his worship. For it seemeth that Sir Palomides is passing envious.'

'Then shall he never win worship,' said the queen, 'for, an it happen an envious man once to win worship, he shall be dishonoured twice therefore. And for this cause all men of worship hate an envious man and will show him no favour.

But he that is courteous and kind and gentle hath favour in every place.'

Now Sir Palomides rode with the two kings and lodged with them that night. And on the morn Sir Palomides departed from them, whereof they were heavy. Then the king of Wales lent a man of his to Sir Palomides and gave him a great courser, and the king of Scotland gave him great gifts. And fain would they have had him abide with them, but he would not in no wise.

And so he departed, and rode as adventure would guide him till it was high noon. And then in a forest by a well Sir Palomides saw where lay a fair wounded knight and his horse bounden by him. And that knight made the greatest dole that ever he heard man make, for ever he wept and therewith sighed as he would die. Then Sir Palomides rode near him and saluted him mildly and said:

'Fair knight, why wail ye so? Let me lie down by you and wail also, for, doubt me not, I am much more heavier than ye are. I dare say that my sorrow is a hundred fold more than yours is. And therefore let us complain either to other.'

'First,' said the wounded knight, 'I require you tell me your name. For an thou be none of the noble knights, thou shalt never know my name whatsomever come of me.'

'Fair knight,' said Sir Palomides, 'such as I am, be it better or be it worse, wit thou well that my name is Sir Palomides, son and heir unto Lord Esclabor; and Sir Safere and Sir Segwarides are my two brethren. And wit thou well, as for myself I was never christened; but my two brethren are truly christened.'

'Ah noble knight,' said that wounded knight, 'well is me that I have met with you. And wit thou well that my name

7 **King Mark mortally wounds Sir Tristram** (*see page* 192)

8 **Sir Dinadan brings the arms of Sir Tristram to King Arthur and Queen Guinevere** (*see page* 196)

is Sir Epinogris, the king's son of Northumberland. Now sit ye down, and let us either complain to other.'

Then Sir Palomides alit and tied his horse fast; and thus he began his complaint and said:

'Now shall I tell you what woe I endure. I love the fairest queen and lady that ever bore life; and wit you well her name is La Beale Iseult, King Mark's wife of Cornwall.'

'That is great folly,' said Sir Epinogris, 'for to love Queen Iseult. For one of the best knights of the world loveth her, that is Sir Tristram de Lyones.'

'That is truth,' said Sir Palomides, 'for no man knoweth that matter better than I do. For I have been in Sir Tristram's fellowship this month and more and with La Beale Iseult together. And alas, unhappy man that I am, now have I lost the fellowship of Sir Tristram and the love of La Beale Iseult for ever, and I am never likely to see her more. And Sir Tristram and I be either to other mortal enemies.'

'Well,' said Sir Epinogris, 'sith that ye loved La Beale Iseult, loved she ever you again by anything that ye could wit, or else did ye ever rejoice her in any pleasure?'

'Nay, by my knighthood,' said Sir Palomides, 'for I never espied that she loved me more than all the world did, nor never had I pleasure with her; but the last day she gave me the greatest rebuke that ever I had, which shall never go from my heart. And yet I well deserved that rebuke, for I did not knightly; and therefore have I lost the love of her and of Sir Tristram for ever. And I have many times enforced myself to do many deeds of arms for her sake, and ever she was the cause of my worship-winning. And alas! Now have I lost all the worship that ever I won; for never shall befall me such prowess as I had in the fellowship of Sir Tristram.'

F

'Nay, nay,' said Sir Epinogris, 'your sorrow is but japes to my sorrow. For I rejoiced my lady, and won her with my hands, and lost her again: alas that day! And first thus I won her. My lady was an earl's daughter; and, as the earl and two knights came home from the tournament of Lonazep, for her sake I set upon this earl myself and on his two knights, my lady there being present. And so by fortune there I slew the earl and one of the knights, and the other knight fled. And so that night I had my lady.

'And on the morn, as she and I reposed us at this well-side, then came there to me an errant knight hight Sir Helyor le Prewse, an hardy knight, and he challenged me to fight for my lady. And then we went to battle, first upon horseback and after upon foot, but at the last Sir Helyor wounded me so that he left me for dead; and so he took my lady with him. And thus my sorrow is more than yours, for I have rejoiced and ye never rejoiced.'

'That is truth,' said Sir Palomides, 'and sith I cannot recover myself, I shall promise you, if I can meet with Sir Helyor, that I shall get to you your lady again, or else he shall beat me.'

Then Sir Palomides made Sir Epinogris to take his horse; and so they rode unto an hermitage. And there Sir Epinogris rested him. And in the meanwhile Sir Palomides walked privily out to rest him under the leaves; and there he saw a knight come riding with a black shield, and that knight hoved under the leaves for heat.

And anon after there came a knight with a green shield and therein a white lion, leading a lady upon a palfrey. And then the knight with the black shield rode fiercely after him, and bade him defend his lady.

'I will defend her,' said he, 'unto my power.'

And so they ran together so mightily that either smote other down, horse and all, to the earth. And then they drew swords, and lashed together wondrous fiercely; but the knight with the black shield was far bigger and smote down the other knight. And then he unlaced his helm to have stricken off his head. And then he cried mercy and bade him take his lady.

And all this Sir Palomides saw and beheld. And then he dressed him up, because he wist well that that same lady was Sir Epinogris' lady. Then he went straight to her and took her by the hand and asked her whether she knew a knight which was called Sir Epinogris.

'Alas,' she said, 'that ever I knew him or he me! For I have for his sake lost my worship and also his life. And that grieveth me most of all.'

'Not so, fair lady,' said Sir Palomides, 'come thou on with me, for here is Sir Epinogris in this hermitage.'

'Ah, well is me,' said the lady, 'an he be on live!'

Then came that other knight and said: 'Whither wilt thou with that lady?'

'I will do with her what me list,' said Sir Palomides.

'Wit thou well,' said the knight, 'thou speakest over-large; though thee seemest thou hast me at advantage, because thou sawest me do battle but late. Thou weenest, sir knight, to have that lady away from me so lightly? Nay, think it never! An thou wert as good a knight as is Sir Lancelot or Sir Tristram or else Sir Palomides, yet thou shalt win her more dearer than ever did I.'

And so they went unto battle on foot. And there they gave many sad strokes together, and either wounded other wonderly sore. And thus they fought together still more than an hour. Then Sir Palomides had marvel what knight he might be that was so strong and so well-breathed during, and he said: 'Knight, I require thee tell me thy name!'

'Wit thou well,' said the knight, 'I dare tell thee my name, so that thou wilt tell me thy name. And truly my name is Sir Safere, son of King Esclabor, and Sir Palomides and Sir Segwarides are my brethren.'

'Now, and wit thou well, my name is Sir Palomides.'

Then Sir Safere kneeled down upon his knees and prayed him of mercy; and then they unlaced their helms and either kissed other weeping. And the meanwhile Sir Epinogris arose out of his bed, for he heard them by the strikes, and so he armed him to help Sir Palomides, if need were. Then Sir Palomides took the lady by the hand and brought her to Sir Epinogris, and there was great joy betwixt them; and either swooned for joy when they were met.

'Now, fair knight and lady,' said Sir Safere, 'it were pity to depart you two, and therefore Jesu send you joy either of other!'

'Gramercy, gentle knight,' said Sir Epinogris, 'and much more thanks to my lord, Sir Palomides, that thus hath through his prowess made me to get my lady.'

Then Sir Epinogris required Sir Palomides and Sir Safere to ride with him unto his castle for the safeguard of his person.

'Sir,' said Sir Palomides, 'we will be ready to conduct you because that ye are sore wounded.'

And so was Sir Epinogris and his lady horsed upon a soft ambler, and then they rode unto his castle. And there they had great cheer and great joy as ever Sir Palomides and Sir Safere had in their lives.

XIX

The Counsels of Blaise

So on the morn Sir Safere and Sir Palomides departed, and rode but as fortune led them; and so they rode all that day until after noon. And at the last they heard a great weeping and a great noise down in a manor.

'Sir,' said Sir Safere, 'let us wit what noise this is.'

'I will well,' said Sir Palomides.

So they rode till they came to a fair gate of a manor, and there sat an old man, saying his prayers and beads. Then Sir Palomides and Sir Safere alit and left their horses and went within the gates. And there they saw full goodly men weeping many.

'Now, fair sirs,' said Sir Palomides, 'wherefore weep ye and make this sorrow?'

And anon one of the knights of the manor beheld Sir Palomides and knew him; and then he went to his fellows and said: 'Fair fellows, wit you well all, we have here the same knight that slew our lord at Lonazep, for I know him well for Sir Palomides.'

Then they went unto harness, all that might bear harness and some on horseback and some on foot, to the number of three score. And when they were ready they came freshly upon Sir Palomides and upon Sir Safere with a great noise, and said:

'Keep thee, Sir Palomides, for thou art known! And by

right thou must be dead, for thou hast slain our lord; and therefore wit thou well we may do thee none other favour but slay thee. And therefore defend thee.'

Then Sir Palomides and Sir Safere, the one set his back to the other, and gave many sad strokes, and also took many great strokes. And thus they fought with twenty knights and forty gentlemen and yeomen nigh on two hours. But at the last though they were never so loth, Sir Palomides and Sir Safere were taken, and put in a strong prison.

And within three days twelve knights passed upon[1] them, and they found Sir Palomides guilty, and Sir Safere not guilty, of their lord's death. And when Sir Safere should be delivered, there was great dole between his brother and him. And of many piteous complaints that was made at their departition there is no maker[2] can rehearse the tenth part.

'Now, fair brother,' said Sir Palomides, 'let be your dolour and your sorrow, for, an I be ordained to die a shameful death, welcome be it. But, an I had wist of this death that I am condemned unto, I should never have been taken on live.'

So departed Sir Safere, with the greatest sorrow that ever made knight. And on the morn they of the castle ordained twelve knights for to ride with Sir Palomides unto the father of the same knight that Sir Palomides slew. And so they bound his legs under an old steed's belly, and then they rode with Sir Palomides unto a castle by the seaside that hight Pylownes; and there Sir Palomides should have his justice. That was their ordinance.

And so they rode with Sir Palomides fast by the castle of Joyous Garde; and, as they passed by that castle, there came riding one of that castle by them that knew Sir Palomides.

[1] passed sentence on. [2] storyteller.

And when that knight saw him led bounden upon a crooked courser, then the knight asked Sir Palomides for what cause he was so led.

'Ah, my fair fellow and knight,' said Sir Palomides, 'I ride now towards my death for the slaying of a knight at the tournament of Lonazep. And if I had not departed from my lord, Sir Tristram, as I ought not to have done, now might I have been sure to have had my life saved. But I pray you, sir knight, recommend me unto my lord, Sir Tristram, and unto my lady, Queen Iseult, and say to them, if ever I trespassed to them, I ask for forgiveness. And also I beseech you recommend me unto my lord, King Arthur, and to all the fellowship of the Round Table.'

Then the knight wept for pity; and therewith he rode unto Joyous Garde as fast as his horse might run. And lightly that knight descended down off his horse and went unto Sir Tristram; and there he told him all as ye have heard. And ever the knight wept as he were wood. And when Sir Tristram heard how Sir Palomides went to his deathward, he was heavy to hear thereof, and said: 'Howbeit that I am wroth with him, yet I will not suffer him to die so shameful a death; for he is a full noble knight.'

And anon Sir Tristram asked his arms. And when he was armed he took his horse and two squires with him, and rode a great pace through the forest after Sir Palomides the next way unto the castle Pylownes where Sir Palomides was judged to his death.

Now, as the twelve knights led him before them, there was the noble knight, Sir Lancelot, that was alit by a well, and had tied his horse to a tree, and had taken off his helm to drink of that well. And when he saw such a rout which seemed knights, Sir Lancelot put on his helm and suffered them to pass by him. And anon he was ware of Sir Palomides bound and led shamefully toward his death.

'Ah Jesu!' said Sir Lancelot, 'what misfortune is befallen him that he is there led towards his death? And therefore I will help him whatsomever come of it, or else I shall die for his sake.'

And then Sir Lancelot mounted on his horse and gat his spear in his hand and rode after the twelve knights that led Sir Palomides.

'Fair knights,' said Sir Lancelot, 'whither lead ye that knight? For it beseemeth him full evil to ride bound.'

Then these twelve knights returned suddenly their horses and said to Sir Lancelot: 'Sir knight, we counsel you not to meddle of this knight, for he hath deserved death and unto death he is judged.'

Then they began to dress their spears: and Sir Lancelot smote the foremost down, horse and man, and so he served three more with one spear. And then that spear brast; and therewithal Sir Lancelot drew his sword, and then he smote on the right hand and on the left hand. And so within a while he left none of those knights but that he had laid them to the earth; and the most part of them were sore wounded. And then Sir Lancelot took the best horse, and loosed Sir Palomides, and set him upon that horse; and so they turned again to Joyous Garde.

And then was Sir Palomides ware of Sir Tristram how he came riding. And when Sir Lancelot saw him he knew him well: but Sir Tristram knew not him because he had on his shoulder a golden shield. So Sir Lancelot made him ready to joust with Sir Tristram because he should not ween that he were Sir Lancelot. Then Sir Palomides cried out loud to Sir Tristram and said: 'Ah, my lord, I require you, joust not with this knight, for he hath saved me from my death.'

When Sir Tristram heard him say so, he came a soft trotting pace toward him. Then said Sir Palomides:

'My lord, Sir Tristram, much am I beholden to you of your great goodness that would proffer your noble body to rescue me undeserved, for much have I offended you. Notwithstanding, here met me with this noble knight that worshipfully and manly rescued me from twelve knights, and smote them down all and sore wounded them.'

'Fair knight,' said Sir Tristram unto Sir Lancelot, 'of whence be ye?'

'I am a knight errant,' said Sir Lancelot, 'that rideth to seek many deeds, and as at this time I will not tell you my name. But now, since ye two are met together either with other, I will depart from you.'

'Not so,' said Sir Tristram, 'I require you, as ye be a lone knight to the Order of Knighthood, play you with me this night.'

Then Sir Tristram had a grant of Sir Lancelot. And when they were come within Joyous Garde they alit, and their horses were led into a stable, and then they unarmed them. And as for Sir Lancelot, as soon as his helm was off, Sir Tristram and Sir Palomides knew him. Then Sir Tristram took Sir Lancelot in his arms, and so did La Beale Iseult; and Sir Palomides kneeled down upon his knees and thanked Sir Lancelot. And when he saw Sir Palomides kneel he lightly took him up and said thus:

'Wit thou well, Sir Palomides, that I, and any knight in this land of worship, must of very right succour and rescue so noble a knight as ye are proved and renowned throughout all this realm, endlong and overthwart.'

Then was there great joy among them. And Sir Lancelot within three or four days departed, and with him rode Sir Gareth and Sir Dinadan. And Sir Palomides was left there with Sir Tristram a two months or more. And the oftener that Sir Palomides saw La Beale Iseult, the heavier he waxed day by day.

And ever Sir Palomides faded and mourned, for all his love and his thought was set upon Queen Iseult that he might neither eat nor drink; so that all men had marvel wherefore he faded so away.

So upon a day in the dawning, Sir Palomides went into the forest by himself alone. And there he found a well; and anon he looked into the well, and in the water he saw his own visage, how he was discoloured and defaded,[1] and nothing like as he was.

'Lord Jesus, what may this mean?' said Sir Palomides. And thus he said to himself:

'Ah, Palomides, Palomides, why art thou thus defaded, that ever was wont to be called one of the fairest knights of the world? Forsooth I will no more live this life; for I love that I may never get nor recover.'

And therewithal he laid him down by the well, and so began to make a rhyme of La Beale Iseult and of Sir Tristram. Now in the meanwhile Sir Tristram was ridden into the same forest to chase an hart of grace;[2] and as he rode he heard one sing, now low, now marvellously loud, as the song led him.

And then Sir Tristram rode softly thither, and descended

[1] worn out.   [2] stag of 6 years and upwards in prime condition.

down from his horse and tied his horse fast to a tree; and so he came near on foot. And soon after he was ware where lay Sir Palomides by the well and sang loud and sweetly. And ever the complaints were of La Beale Iseult which was marvellously well said, and piteously and full dolefully made. And all the whole song Sir Tristram heard, word by word. And when he had heard all Sir Palomides' complaint, he was wroth out of measure, and thought for to slay him where he lay.

Then Sir Tristram remembered himself that Sir Palomides was unarmed, and of the so noble a name that Sir Palomides had, and also the noble name that himself had. Then he made a restraint of his anger; and so he went unto Sir Palomides a soft pace, and said:

'Sir Palomides, I have heard your complaint and of your treason that ye have owed me long; and wit you well, therefore, ye shall die! And if it were not for shame of knighthood, thou shouldest not escape my hands: for now I know well thou hast awaited me with treason. And therefore tell me how thou wilt acquit thee.'

'Sir, I shall acquit me thus. As for Queen Iseult, thou shalt wit that I love her above all other ladies in this world. And well I wot it shall befall by me as for her love befell to the noble knight, Sir Kehydius, that died for love of La Beale Iseult. And now, Sir Tristram, I will that ye wit that I have loved La Beale Iseult many a long day, and she hath been the causer of all my worship. For by her, and because of her, I have won the worship that I have: for, when I remembered me of Queen Iseult, I won the worship wheresomever I came for the most part. And yet I had never reward nor bounty of her, and I have been her knight long guerdonless. And therefore, Sir Tristram, as for any death I dread not, for I would as soon die as live.'

'Sir, well have ye uttered your treason,' said Sir Tristram.

'Sir, I have done you no treason,' said Sir Palomides, 'for love is free for all men. And, though I have loved your lady, she is my lady as well as yours. Howbeit it is I have wrong, if any wrong there be: for ye rejoice her and have your desire of her, and so had I never nor never am like to have.'

'Then,' said Sir Tristram, 'I will fight with you to the utterest.'

'I grant,' said Sir Palomides, 'for in a better quarrel hope I never to fight. For, an I die of your hands, of a better knight's hands might I never be slain.'

'Then set ye a day,' said Sir Tristram, 'that we shall do battle.'

'Sir, this day fifteen days,' said Sir Palomides, 'I will meet with you hereby in the meadow under Joyous Garde.'

'Now fie for shame!' said Sir Tristram, 'Will ye set so long a day? Let us fight to-morn.'

'Not so,' said Sir Palomides, 'for I am meagre and have been long sick for the love of La Beale Iseult. And therefore I will repose me till I have my strength again.'

So then Sir Tristram and Sir Palomides promised faithfully to meet at the well that day fifteen days.

'But now I am remembered,' said Sir Tristram to Sir Palomides, 'that ye brake me once a promise when that I rescued you from Sir Breuse-sans-Pité and nine knights. And then ye promised to meet me at the perron and the grave beside Camelot, whereas at that time ye failed of your promise.'

'Wit you well,' said Sir Palomides, 'I was at that day in

prison, that I might not hold my promise. But wit you well, I shall promise you now and keep it.'

'So God me help,' said Sir Tristram, 'an ye had holden your promise, this work had not been here now at this time.'

Right so departed Sir Tristram and Sir Palomides. And so Sir Palomides took his horse and his harness and so he rode unto King Arthur's court. And there he gat him four knights and four sergeants-at-arms, and so he returned again toward Joyous Garde.

And so in the meanwhile Sir Tristram chased and hunted at all manner of venery. And about three days before the battle should be, as Sir Tristram chased an hart, there was an archer shot at the hart; and by misfortune he smote Sir Tristram in the thick of the thigh, and the same arrow slew Sir Tristram's horse under him.

When Sir Tristram was so hurt, he was passing heavy; and wit you well he bled passing sore. And then he took another horse and rode unto Joyous Garde with great heaviness, more for the promise that he had made unto Sir Palomides than for any hurt. Wherefore there was neither man nor woman could cheer him with anything that they could make to him; for ever he deemed that Sir Palomides had smitten him so that he should not be able to do battle with him at the day appointed. But in no wise there was no knight about Sir Tristram that would believe that Sir Palomides would hurt him, neither by his own hands nor by none other consenting.

And so when the fifteenth day was come, Sir Palomides came to the well with the knights and the sergeants-at-arms. And for this intent he brought them with him, that they should bear record of the battle betwixt Sir Tristram and him. So Sir Palomides came into the field and there he abode nigh two hours; and then he sent a squire unto Sir Tristram and desired him to come into the field to hold his promise.

When the squire was come unto Joyous Garde, anon as Sir Tristram heard of his coming he commanded that the squire should come to his presence thereas he lay in his bed.

'My lord, Sir Tristram,' said the squire, 'wit you well, my lord, Sir Palomides, abideth you in the field, and he would wit whether ye would do battle or not.'

'Ah my fair brother,' said Sir Tristram, 'wit you well that I am right heavy for these tidings. But tell your lord, Sir Palomides, an I were well at ease, I would not lie here; nor should he have had no need to send for me, an I might either ride or go.'

And for that he should see that he was no liar, Sir Tristram showed him his thigh, and the depth of the wound was six inches deep.

'And now thou hast seen my hurt,' said Sir Tristram, 'tell thy lord that this is no feigned matter; and tell him that I had liefer than all the gold that King Arthur hath that I were whole. And let him wit that as for me, as soon as I may ride, I shall seek him endlong and overthwart this land: and that I promise you as I am a true knight. And, if ever I may meet him, tell your lord, Sir Palomides, he shall have of me his fill of battle.'

And so the squire departed. And when Sir Palomides knew that Sir Tristram was hurt, then departed Sir Palomides where fortune led him. And within a month Sir Tristram was whole of his hurt; and then he took his horse and rode from country to country, and always he enquired for Sir Palomides. But of all that quarter of summer Sir Tristram could never meet with Sir Palomides.

And therefore Sir Tristram resorted again unto Joyous Garde whereas La Beale Iseult was that loved him ever.

As for Sir Palomides, it chanced on a day that he came to the forest of Broceliande; and therein he wandered long ere he could find shelter, and at eve he came to an hermitage. And Sir Palomides alit from his horse and tied him to a tree, and went towards the hermitage. And the hermit that was therein came forth to meet him, and he was an old man, and leant upon a staff, and he greeted Sir Palomides and said: 'Welcome, Sir Palomides, the Saracen, that art but half a knight and half a lover, and half a man.'

'Who art thou?' said Sir Palomides, 'and how knowest thou me?'

'I am Blaise,' said he, 'that was Merlin's master. And I know you better than ye think. And true it is that ye be but half a knight, for a quest ye have but stay not in it. And ye are but half a lover for your love is but a lust of the eye and cometh not from the heart. And for that ye believe but are not christened ye are but the half of a man.'

'Alas, that is truth,' said Sir Palomides, 'that I have left my quest and am not christened. Yet have I been true to my love.'

'Not so,' said the hermit, 'for though ye dote upon Queen Iseult when ye behold her or when ye ride at adventure, yet ye think not of her when ye are about your quest. And now must ye leave this love, for she is the wife of one and the lover of another, and no part have ye in these matters.'

'Ah, woe is me,' said Sir Palomides, 'a sinful man am I, but how may I leave this love?'

'Leave it ye must,' said the hermit, 'and in truth ye must learn that it is but lust and pride and envy of Sir Tristram, and it is not for thee. But come within and abide with me that I may tell thee what thou must do.'

So Sir Palomides went with the hermit and abode with him for many days. And Blaise taught him many things, and told him that never again should he see Queen Iseult in this life; and that soon many knights of the Table Round would go forth upon an holy quest, but he must go upon the quest of the Beast. And as yet he would not baptize Sir Palomides for the vow that he had taken.

And at the last Blaise sent him forth again out of the forest and said:

'Great deeds have ye done, but ever ye fail at the greatest. For your strength increases not by faith but with madness, and at the end it changeth to despair. Soon shall ye find this last fight that shall release you from your vow. And then be ye christened, for ye cannot achieve the Questing Beast alone, but only by God's help. And at the end, if ye heed my words, perchance also ye may find true love.'

Then he blessed him, and Sir Palomides went on his way.

XX

The Christening of Sir Palomides

Now on a day King Arthur proclaimed a great feast at
the Pentecost next following. And all his knights were
summoned to that feast. And Sir Tristram rode
toward Camelot with no harness of war but his spear and his
sword. And, as he rode, he saw afore him two knights that
jousted; and one knight struck down the other, horse and man
to the earth. And Sir Tristram saw that he that had the
victory was Sir Palomides. Then Sir Tristram repented him
that he was not armed, and therewith he hoved still. And
anon, as Sir Palomides saw Sir Tristram, he cried on high:
'Sir Tristram, now be we met, for or we depart we shall
redress all the old sorrows.'

'As for that,' said Sir Tristram, 'there was never yet no
Christian man that ever might make his boast that ever I fled
from him. And wit thou well, Sir Palomides, thou that art a
Saracen shall never make thy boast that ever Sir Tristram de
Lyones shall flee from thee.'

And therewith Sir Tristram made his horse to run, and with
all his might he came straight upon Sir Palomides and brast
his spear upon him in an hundred pieces. And forthwithal Sir
Tristram drew his sword; and then he turned his horse and
struck together six great strikes upon his helm. And Sir
Palomides stood still and beheld Sir Tristram, and marvelled
greatly at his woodness and of his folly. And then Sir Palo-

mides said to himself: 'An this Sir Tristram were armed, it were hard to cease him from his battle; and, if I turn again and slay him, I am shamed wherever I go.'

Then Sir Tristram spake and said: 'Thou coward knight, what castest thou to do? And why wilt thou not do battle with me? For have thou no doubt I shall endure thee.'

'Ah, Sir Tristram,' said Sir Palomides, 'full well thou wotest I may not have ado with thee for shame, for thou art here naked and I am armed. And, if that I slay thee, dishonour shall be mine. Now I require you tell me a question that I shall say unto you.'

'Then tell me what it is,' said Sir Tristram, 'and I shall answer you of the truth, as God me help.'

'Sir, I put case,' said Sir Palomides, 'that ye were armed at all rights as well as I am, and I naked as ye be. What would ye do to me now, by your true knighthood?'

'Ah,' said Sir Tristram, 'now I understand thee well, Sir Palomides, for now must I say mine own judgement! And, as God me bless, that I shall say shall not be said for no fear that I have of thee. But this is all: wit thou well, Sir Palomides, as at this time thou shouldst depart from me, for I would not have ado with thee.'

'No more will I,' said Sir Palomides, 'and therefore ride forth on thy way!'

'As for that,' said Sir Tristram, 'I may choose either to ride or to go. But, Sir Palomides, I marvel greatly of one thing: that thou that art so good a knight wilt not be christened; and thy brother, Sir Safere, hath been christened many a day.'

'As for that,' said Sir Palomides, 'I may not yet be christened for a vow that I made many years agone. Howbeit in my heart and in my soul I have had many a day a good belief in

Jesu Christ and his mild Mother Mary. But I have but one battle to do, and, were that one done, I would be baptized.'

'By my head,' said Sir Tristram, 'as for one battle, thou shalt not seek it long. For God defend that through my default thou shouldst longer live a Saracen. Yonder is the knight that ye have hurt and smitten down. Now help me then that I were armed in his armour, and I shall soon fulfil thy vow.'

'As ye will,' said Sir Palomides, 'so shall it be.'

So they rode both unto that knight that sat upon a bank; and then Sir Tristram saluted him, and he weakly saluted him again.

'Sir Knight,' said Sir Tristram, 'I require you to tell me your right name. Also I must pray you to lend me your whole armour, for I must do battle with this knight.'

'Sir,' he said, 'my right name is Sir Galleron of Galloway, and a knight of the Table Round. As for my armour, ye shall have it with a good will. But ye must beware, for I warn you that this knight is an hardy knight as ever I met withal. Now I pray you tell me your name, and what is that knight's name that has beaten me.'

'So God me help,' said Sir Tristram, 'I am right heavy of your hurts. As for my name, wit thou well it is Sir Tristram de Lyones; and his name is Sir Palomides, brother unto the good knight Sir Safere; and yet is Sir Palomides unchristened.'

'Alas!' said Sir Galleron, 'that is great pity that so good a knight and so noble a man of arms should be unchristened.'

'So God me help,' said Sir Tristram, 'either he shall slay me or I him but that he shall be christened or ever we depart in sunder.'

Then Sir Tristram unarmed Sir Galleron; and as well as he might Sir Galleron armed Sir Tristram, for he was sore hurt.

And then Sir Tristram mounted upon his horse, and in his hand he gat Sir Galleron's spear; and therewithal Sir Palomides was ready. And so they came hurtling together, and either smote other in midst of their shields. And therewithal Sir Palomides' spear brake; and Sir Tristram smote down Sir Palomides, horse and man to the earth.

And then Sir Palomides, as soon as he might, avoided his horse, and dressed his shield and pulled out his sword. That saw Sir Tristram, and therewithal he alit and tied his horse to a tree. And then they came together eagerly as two wild boars, and so they lashed together, tracing and traversing as noble men that often had been proved in battle. And thus they fought more than two hours. And often times Sir Tristram smote such strokes at Sir Palomides that he made him to kneel; and Sir Palomides brake and cut many pieces off Sir Tristram's shield. And then Sir Palomides wounded Sir Tristram passing sore, for he was a well-fighting man.

Then Sir Tristram waxed wood wroth out of measure, and rushed upon Sir Palomides with such a might that Sir Palomides fell grovelling to the earth. And therewithal he leapt up lightly upon his feet, and then Sir Tristram wounded sore Sir Palomides through the shoulder. And ever Sir Tristram failed him not, but gave him many sad strokes again. And at the last Sir Tristram doubled his strokes upon him; and by fortune Sir Tristram smote Sir Palomides' sword out of his hand. And, if Sir Palomides had stooped for his sword, he had been slain. And then Sir Palomides stood still and beheld his sword with a sorrowful heart.

'How now?' said Sir Tristram. 'For now I have thee at advantage as thou hadst me this day: but it shall never be said in no court nor among no good knights that Sir Tristram shall slay any knight that is weaponless. And therefore take thou thy sword, and let us make an end of this battle.'

'As for to do this battle,' said Sir Palomides, 'I dare right well end it. But I have no great lust to fight no more, and for this cause: my offence is to you not so great but that we may be friends, for all that I have offended is and was for the love of La Beale Iseult. And as for her, I proffered her never no manner of dishonour. And sithen I had offended never as to her own person and as for the offence that I have done it was against your own person, and for that offence ye have given me this day many sad strokes, and some I have given you again—wherefore I require you, my lord, forgive me all that I have offended unto you. And this same day have me to the next church; and first let me be clean confessed, and after that see yourself that I be truly baptized. And then will we ride together to the court of King Arthur, that we may be there at the next high feast following.'

'Then take your horse,' said Sir Tristram, 'and, as ye say, so shall it be. And, as for your offences, may God forgive you as I do too. And hereby within this mile is the suffragan of Carlisle, which shall give you the sacrament of baptism.'

And anon they took their horses, and Sir Galleron rode with them; and when they came to the suffragan, Sir Tristram told him their desire. Then the suffragan let fill a great vessel with water, and when he had hallowed it he then confessed clean Sir Palomides. And Tristram and Sir Galleron were his godfathers.

And then soon after they departed and rode toward Camelot, where that King Arthur and Queen Guinevere were, and the most part of all the knights of the Round Table were there also. And so the king and all the court were right glad that Sir Palomides was christened.

And then were they all called unto the feast. And at that same feast came Sir Galahad, that was son unto Sir Lancelot du Lake, and sat in the Siege Perilous.

And as they sat at meat there came in the Holy Grail and passed before them through the hall. And the most part of the knights that were there took avows after Sir Gawaine to go in quest of the Holy Vessel, and with them Sir Tristram made his vow. But Sir Palomides took not the vow, for he was mindful of the words of the holy hermit. And so thereafter withal they departed and dissevered, all the knights of the Round Table.

And as Sir Palomides rode upon his way, there met him Sir Dinadan, and each greeted other.

'Welcome ye be,' said Sir Palomides, 'but, an ye ride on this quest of the Sangreal, ride not with me; for I ride upon another quest.'

'A plague upon that quest,' said Sir Dinadan, 'I will none of it. For only ill will come of it save for him that shall achieve it. And that, I ween, shall be Sir Lancelot or his son, Sir Galahad.'

And as they rode, they saw afar off where lay a knight sore wounded, and a damsel that tended him. And ere they might come to the place, they saw two knights come out of a wood. And the one of them challenged the wounded knight to joust; and scarce might he rise nor sit upon his horse. And that other knight rode a great wallop against the wounded knight and smote him from his horse, and rode over him twice or thrice.

'That was foully done,' said Sir Palomides.

Then he put spurs to his horse and rode swiftly against that knight, and when he was nigh, he saw that it was Sir Gawaine. Then Sir Palomides cried on high that he would joust with him. And so they came together like thunder. And Sir Palomides smote Sir Gawaine, horse and man to earth. And then he rode over him and said: 'A foul deed hast thou done and an unknightly. Now is thy evil will requited.'

Then Sir Gawaine cried aloud to him that rode with him and said, 'Sir Gareth, my brother, why dost thou not avenge me?'

'I will not so,' said Sir Gareth, 'for thou hast thy deserts.'

Then was Sir Gawaine wroth and said: 'I know thee, Sir Palomides the Saracen. In an ill hour for thee are we meet. For now I make mine avow that I will slay thee for this despite thou hast done me.'

So Sir Gawaine took his horse and departed as at that time.

Then Sir Palomides greeted Sir Gareth and the wounded knight. And then he saw that that knight was Sir Segwarides, his brother, and the damsel was the Lady Iverna, the wife of Sir Segwarides. Then Sir Palomides alit and kissed his brother and the lady, and asked them what had befallen.

'In truth,' said Sir Segwarides, 'we rode upon our way when there met us a knight that greeted us and rode with us. And, as we rode, on a sudden the knight cried to me to look to my lady, and drew a little aback. And as I turned me he thrust me through the body with a sword between the joints of the harness, so that I fell from my horse. And when he would alight for to slay me, then he heard a noise of horses, that was Sir Gawaine and Sir Gareth; and there he turned his horse and fled away swiftly. And then by his riding I knew him for Sir Breuse-sans-Pité, an enemy to all good knights.'

'Would I knew where he were become,' said Sir Gareth, 'for he is a destroyer of knights and ladies, and long have I vowed to destroy him.'

'In very truth he will return,' said Iverna. 'But he will not come nigh if ye be by. Yet, an ye leave us, I fear for my lord that he will slay him swiftly ere ye can succour us.'

'Then must we use a stratagem,' said Sir Palomides. 'I will hide me in this great tree that is near by. And ye, Sir Gareth and Sir Dinadan, hide you upon your horses in the woods at either end of this place, and we will see what may befall.'

And so they did. And soon thereafter came Sir Breuse, riding stealthily to the edge of the forest. And when he saw nought but Sir Segwarides and the lady, then he rode swiftly toward them. And when he came up to them, Sir Palomides leapt lightly from the tree and cried: 'Stay thee, thou felon knight, Sir Breuse! For now art thou come to thine end.'

And for all Sir Palomides was afoot, Sir Breuse feared him overmuch; and he turned his horse to flee. But there in the way came Sir Dinadan with his spear in rest. Thereat Sir Breuse turned him about and put spurs to his horse. But, as he turned he was ware of Sir Gareth that rode full upon him. And since he had no resort he feutred his spear and rode upon Sir Gareth. And they two met together, and Sir Gareth smote Sir Breuse so sore that his spear went clean through his body and laid him stark dead upon the earth.

Then they took up Sir Segwarides and bore him to a castle near by to be healed of his wounds. And Sir Palomides abode with him. But Sir Dinadan said he would ride to seek Sir Tristram; and Sir Gareth departed with him. And when Sir Segwarides was something healed of his wounds then Sir Palomides and the Lady Iverna rode with him to the castle of

their father, Lord Esclabor. And greatly he rejoiced to see his
sons, and made them good cheer. And so they abode at that
time.

XXI

The Treachery of Sir Gawaine

Now King Mark had sent oft unto King Arthur and entreated him that he would send back La Beale Iseult into Cornwall. But King Arthur would not for love of Sir Tristram and for fear of the Lineage of Ban that held ever with Sir Tristram. And when King Mark saw how the great part of the knights of the Round Table were abroad on the quest of the Grail, then King Mark sent an ambassage unto the Saxons, that were mortal foes to King Arthur, and agreed with them to make war upon the realm of Logres.

So the Saxons came with a great army to Synedoc, and there King Mark met them with the army of Cornwall. And thence they marched swiftly and secretly; and they pillaged no town, that King Arthur might not be ware of them.

But on the sixth day they came to Joyous Garde, where Queen Iseult was; and all the doors stood open, for they deemed there was nought to fear. And then King Mark entered with six hundred knights and took the queen where she sat among her women. And then for very wrath and for despite of Sir Tristram King Mark made much pillage and slaughter and set fire to the houses. And thereafter the armies of King Mark and of the Saxons went on their way. But there escaped a man from Joyous Garde, who took a swift horse and made speed to Camelot, and told King Arthur of what befell or ever King Mark left his pillage and burning.

Then King Arthur strengthened the walls of Camelot as well as he might, and sent messengers abroad to summon such knights as could be found; and much he grieved that so many had gone upon the quest.

And upon the fourth day after that the tidings reached the king there came in two knights when the king was at the Mass, and told him that the army of Cornwall was near at hand.

So the king armed him and gathered his companies and went out into the field before Camelot. And there his army encountered with King Mark's army. But King Arthur's knights were few, and in all the field they were hard pressed. And when King Arthur was weary, there encountered with him King Mark, and wounded him; and then King Arthur's men pulled him within the city, and all the knights that were left withdrew within the walls and they closed the gates. And so King Mark closely invested the city.

Now the messengers of King Arthur ranged hither and thither, and one came to the Lord Esclabor in his castle. When he had the King's message, then the Lord Esclabor armed himself, though he was very old and had not fought for many years, and likewise did Sir Palomides. And as they rode to Camelot there encountered with them Sir Galahad; and when he heard what was toward they rode all together.

And at last they came to the forest of Camelot; and there there encountered with them four Saxon knights whom they slew, and also a Cornish knight. And they spared the life of that knight if so he would tell them all that had befallen. And thus they learnt that King Arthur had been wounded and was hard pressed in Camelot, for all that King Caradoc with an army had come to aid him. Also that knight said that King

Mark had taken Queen Iseult and sent her under strong guard into Cornwall. Then Sir Palomides asked that knight news of Sir Tristram, but he answered that none knew where he had become, though King Mark sought him alway.

And on the morrow they came to the edge of the forest and looked over the plain to Camelot. And then they heard Mass at a little chapel. And the priest told them that that day King Caradoc would make a great sally with all his men; yet were they many less than the Saxons with King Mark.

So then came King Caradoc from the city and did great deeds. And then Sir Galahad and the Lord Esclabor and Sir Palomides went into the field and wrought great havoc among the Cornishmen. And that saw King Mark, who deemed them knights returned from the quest at adventure, and sought to be rid of them. And he drew near privily and smote the Lord Esclabor and his horse to the ground, and wounded him sore.

And when Sir Palomides saw his father smitten down, then he rode to King Mark and smote him to the earth, and would have slain him but that his knights bore him away. And then King Caradoc and Sir Galahad and Sir Palomides ranged hither and thither, and much slaughter did they make that none might abide them. And all the army of the Saxons and the Cornish that were left fled from the field.

So when Sir Galahad saw that the day was won, he would not stay, but rode into the forest. And King Arthur made much praise of the Lord Esclabor and Sir Palomides.

So when Sir Palomides knew that King Mark had fled into Cornwall and that the Saxons that were left were departed back across the seas, then he bethought him again of his quest, and he took leave of his father and of King Arthur and so departed. And he took no spear with him, but only his sword.

And when Sir Gawaine saw that Sir Palomides rode alone, he thought to have his vengeance. So he summoned his brethren, Sir Agravaine and Sir Mordred; and Sir Uwaine also rode with them but to him Sir Gawaine spoke not of his intent.

So these four knights rode forth and when they had tidings of Sir Palomides they rode swiftly by paths to await him on his way: and when they came upon him they proffered him to joust.

'I have no spear,' said Sir Palomides.

'We will lend you a spear,' said they.

'It is full knightly of you to bring the stick ye shall be beaten withal,' said Sir Palomides.

Now it was Sir Gawaine's intent that they should fall upon him all together, but because of Sir Uwaine he durst not utter his thought. So first Sir Uwaine encountered with Sir Palomides and Sir Palomides gave him so hard a fall that he lay there stunned. And thereafter he smote the other three knights to the earth with the same spear, and so passed on his way.

And at that time there came a knight, and when he saw the jousts he hoved to watch the jousts. And the knight was disguised, but Sir Gawaine knew him for Sir Lancelot. Then Sir Gawaine cried aloud and said to him: 'Sir knight, be thou our avenger. For that false traitor that is but now departed is Sir Breuse-sans-Pité.'

When Sir Lancelot heard that, he rode after Sir Palomides and bade him turn and defend him. So Sir Lancelot and Sir Palomides encountered together, and then either smote other, horse and man, to the earth. And then they rose lightly and drew their swords, and lashed together many mighty strokes. And when they had fought for above two hours, it chanced that Sir Lancelot wounded Sir Palomides sore so that he lost much blood. And when Sir Lancelot saw that he grew weary he said: 'Now yield thee, thou false knight, Sir Breuse-sans-Pité, or else here thou diest.'

And when Sir Palomides heard him so say, he was astonied, and he said:

'In truth little more can I do, for I am sore wounded. But I am Sir Palomides; and I know not wherefore ye call me by the name of that felon, Sir Breuse that of late Sir Gareth hath slain.'

When Sir Lancelot heard that, he let fall his sword and went to Sir Palomides and took him in his arms and craved his pardon.

'For,' said he, 'thou wert falsely called by those knights thou hast but now forjousted.[1] And I am Sir Lancelot, and well I know thy valiance, and woe is me that I have done thee this hurt.'

'My lord, Sir Lancelot,' said Sir Palomides, 'ye are the knight that above all in the world I honour. And this trouble was wrought of malice by Sir Gawaine, and ye are not to blame. Wherefore now leave me that I may go to an hermitage near at hand if peradventure I may be healed. And if I die, Sir Lancelot, pray for my soul!'

Then Sir Lancelot helped Sir Palomides upon his horse and set him upon his way, and so departed. But Sir Gawaine and Sir Agravaine had hid them near by for to see the battle. And when they saw that Sir Lancelot was clean gone, they rode upon Sir Palomides and attacked him both of them together.

[1] defeated in jousting.

'Stay your hands,' said Sir Palomides, 'for I am but now sore wounded in a battle; and it is not knightly for two knights that are fresh to attack one that is sore spent.'

'That shall not avail thee,' said Sir Gawaine, 'wherefore either defend thee as thou mayest, or be slain like an ox as thou standest.'

Then Sir Gawaine struck Sir Palomides a great blow on the helm and Sir Agravaine smote him from behind. And when he drew his sword and essayed to defend himself, his wounds broke out afresh so that he fainted and fell from his horse to the earth.

Then Sir Gawaine leapt lightly down from his horse, and raced off his helm for to have smitten off his head. But Sir Agravaine cried:

'Stay brother! Enough ill have ye done already. He is beyond hope of life and I would not for all the world that we cut off the head of so good a knight. Let us leave him, for too much have we done.'

'Since it is your will,' said Sir Gawaine, 'I will not smite off his head. Yet he shall not escape me.'

And so saying, Sir Gawaine lifted the hauberk of Sir Palomides and thrust his sword through his body. And so Sir Gawaine and Sir Agravaine departed.

Now turn we to the Lord Esclabor, that yearned for his son, Sir Palomides, when that he was departed, and Lord Esclabor had a deeming that some ill would befall Palomides. Wherefore he called his squire, that was but a boy, and bade him saddle their horses; and secretly they two rode forth from Camelot when it was night, though Lord Esclabor was of a great age and his wound was not healed.

And so at last they came where Sir Palomides lay. And when

the Lord Esclabor saw his grisly wounds and that he nor moved nor spake, he deemed him dead, for all that he was still warm. And Lord Esclabor cried aloud and said:

'Alas, my dear son, Sir Palomides! Traitorously hast thou been slain. For there is no knight living that would so have wounded thee in fair fight. Woe is me that am old that I have lived to see this day!'

Then the Lord Esclabor bade the page saddle his horse and ride to the Lady Etain. And then he went to the hermitage that was not far off, and prayed the hermit that he would aid him to make a coffin of rough wood for a good knight that lay dead near at hand.

'And let us make it large enough,' said he, 'for I ween that I too am nigh my death, and I may be buried therein with my dear son.'

'There is no need,' said the hermit, 'for this toil. For here is a coffin of wood fairly made. For myself I wrought it, but as yet I need it not. Now rest ye here awhile, for I must go into the forest to gather herbs. And when I come again, we will bury that dead knight.'

So the hermit departed. And the Lord Esclabor sat him down by the coffin, and sore he wept for Sir Palomides. And he commended him to God, and prayed the Lord Jesu to have mercy on his soul, and besought him to take into his keeping his own soul also.

Then he looked upon the coffin and bethought him to cut thereon the name of Sir Palomides and his own name. And so he took his sword and cut with it upon the wood as best he might; and ever he made lamentation and cried upon the Lord to deliver him from his great grief. And so it was that as he made an end of the name of Palomides, so the Lord had mercy on him, and his heart brake for very sorrow, and he fell down by the coffin stark dead.

And it chanced that there came by the hermitage some men of the forest, and they found the coffin and the old knight dead beside.

'Lo here is one that would be within his coffin,' said they. 'But since he may not bury himself, it were but charity in us to take him to some churchyard that there he may have Christian burial.'

So they put the Lord Esclabor within the coffin, and closed down the lid thereof. And then they bore it between them, and so passed on their way.

G

XXII

The Death of the Lovers in Cornwall

Now when Sir Galahad rode from Camelot after the battle with King Mark, he wandered many days by strange ways that he knew not till at the last he came to a fair Abbey, and there he thought to lodge him for the night. And within that Abbey he found Sir Tristram, and right glad were they of the meeting. And so Sir Galahad told Sir Tristram of the battle, and of how King Mark had taken Queen Iseult and sent her into Cornwall, and was now after the battle himself fled into Cornwall with but thirty knights.

'A plague upon this quest!' said Sir Tristram, 'for it hath brought nought but sorrow upon this realm of Logres. And if so be I may find that false knight, Sir Gawaine, that first took the vow in this quest, I will thrust it down his throat and my sword thereafter.'

And Sir Galahad held his peace. But well he wot that Sir Tristram spake of Logres but that his thought was only upon La Beale Iseult. And on the morrow Sir Galahad and Sir Tristram took their leave and departed each from other.

And at last Sir Tristram reached the sea coast. And there he met Sir Dinadan that had sought him many days through all the land of Logres. And wit you well Sir Dinadan was right glad to see Sir Tristram. But when he wist that Sir Tristram would go into Cornwall, then was Sir Dinadan wroth, and said:

'Oft have I told you, Sir Tristram, that ye are wood mad, and ye would not hearken. But now ye go to your death, for King Mark will not let you go a second time.'

Nevertheless when Sir Tristram would not be moved, Sir Dinadan was accorded to go with him. And so they disguised themselves and took ship and came into Cornwall. And then in secret they went unto the castle of Sir Dinas the Seneschal, that was a friend to Sir Tristram, and there they lodged. And anon Sir Dinas sent secretly unto the queen, to tell her Sir Tristram was there.

So then the queen made a strategem to have Sir Tristram come to her. And so it was that Sir Tristram would come oft to the queen disguised as a gentlewoman. And none knew save one or two that were about the queen.

But on a day, as Sir Tristram was harping, and Queen Iseult singing, there passed by the queen's apartments Sir Andret, that was nephew to King Mark, and ever a foe unto Tristram. And Sir Andret stayed to hearken, for he deemed he knew that harping. And ere the harping ceased when Queen Iseult and Sir Tristram were gone to bed, well wist Sir Andret that the harper was Sir Tristram. And so Sir Andret went and told King Mark.

Now it chanced that the queen could not sleep for foul dreams, and anon she awaked Sir Tristram also; and so they arose out of bed and sat them down to play at chess.

But King Mark was nigh out of his mind for wrath when he heard Sir Andret's tidings. And he seized a sword in his hand that Morgan le Fay had given him, and ran to the queen's apartments with the sword drawn in his hand; but the outer door was shut fast and locked. Then King Mark remembered him of a grille that was above the queen's bed.

So stealthily the King went through the passage till that he came below the grille. And then he fetched a chair that he might stand thereon and so look through the grille.

And when King Mark looked, lo there was none within the bed, but on the other side thereof he beheld the queen and Sir Tristram as they played at chess. And Sir Tristram was without armour and had on him a light silk robe. And Sir Tristram leant over the board to move a piece; and as he moved it he moved a little more over the board to kiss the queen. And when King Mark saw that he hurled the sword through the grille and it struck Sir Tristram on the left thigh and stuck fast.

Then Sir Tristram gave a loud cry and started up and drew out the sword; and well he wist it was King Mark or else Sir Andret that had done this thing. And so he ran out of the queen's chamber all wounded as he was with the sword in his hand, and ran through the palace. And when he might not find them he betook him to the castle of Sir Dinas that his wound might be searched.

But when the doctors and the wise men came and searched the wound there was nought they could do, for the sword was poisoned and deadly. And then tidings was brought to the palace that Sir Tristram was like to die. And Queen Iseult swooned for very sorrow and knew not what to do, for she feared King Mark.

So Sir Tristram, when he knew that he must die, sent unto his uncle King Mark, and prayed him to come unto him. But King Mark would not come, for he was afraid. Then went Sir Dinadan unto King Mark and said:

'A coward ye were ever, but must ye also fear a man that is but a shadow and half dead? And in a foul world wherein

men think of nought but joustings and hackings and wound-
ings without reason, the foulest thing art thou that slayest afar
by stealth. But since my lord, Sir Tristram, would speak with
thee, come thou shalt.'

Then Sir Dinadan seized King Mark and dragged him from
the palace, none letting him, and so he brought him trembling
before Sir Tristram.

'Now mine uncle, King Mark,' said Sir Tristram, 'methinks
ye should have all ye desire. For in truth I, that so oft ye
sought by treachery to slay, am at the point of death. Yet well
I wot the time may come when ye would give the half of
your kingdom to have me with you. But now I charge you
amend your ways, and do no more treason unto my lord,
King Arthur or to his knights. And as for my lady, Queen
Iseult, I will not commend her to you; for ye are not worthy
so much as to look upon her. And so I take my leave of you.'

And King Mark wist not what to say, and answered him
not a word, and anon withdrew him. Yet a little he repented
him of that he had done. Wherefore he bade the queen go
unto Sir Tristram for to make some amends betwixt Sir
Tristram and him. Also he deemed that Sir Tristram might
be dead ere the queen came to him. So Queen Iseult came in
the evening and abode with him all that night. But so weak he
was he scarce might speak.

And at the dawn he sent for Sir Dinadan and bade him
bring his sword and his shield, for that he was taking leave of
knighthood.

'And now, Sir Dinadan,' said Sir Tristram, 'would ye hear
the most shameful word that ever I uttered? Alas, alas, Sir
Dinadan, I cannot make pretence. I yield myself vanquished,
for death hath overcome me.'

And then Sir Tristram fell a-weeping, and Queen Iseult and Sir Dinadan wept also. And at last Sir Tristram said to Sir Dinadan:

'Salute Sir Palomides, with whom I shall fight no more, and Sir Lancelot. And bear my sword and shield unto my lord, King Arthur, for he is my liege lord, and not that recreant, King Mark. Yet say unto King Mark that at the last I forgive him, for I would die at peace. Alas, alas, why must I so soon die? Farewell to you, my good sword. For I cannot bear to look upon you longer.'

Then he turned him to La Beale Iseult and said:

'Ah what will ye do, mine own lady, when I am dead? How shall Iseult live without Tristram? For one of us only to be on live is like unto the fish without the river or the body without the soul. Surely we should have died together, my sweet and lovely love!'

'Ah, my dear lord, Sir Tristram,' said Queen Iseult, 'shame indeed it would be if Tristram died and Iseult lived, for we are one flesh and one heart and one soul. But what to do? For ye may not slay me of intent, and deadly sin it were for me to slay myself.'

'Ye say well,' said Sir Tristram.

Then he bade farewell to Sir Dinadan and Sir Dinas and all them that were there, and bade them leave him alone until he was dead. And he took Queen Iseult into his bed that he might die in her arms. But so it was that at the touch of her body all his strength came back unto him for the last time, and he clypt her and kissed her so fiercely that all unwitting he crushed the life out of her body. And in that same moment Sir Tristram died also.

So when they had waited long time, Sir Dinadan and Sir

Dinas came in and found Sir Tristram and Queen Iseult stark dead. So then Sir Dinadan took Sir Tristram's sword and shield and went his way to King Arthur's court.

Now leave we Sir Dinadan and turn we unto the men that bore Lord Esclabor in his coffin. And it chanced that as they went they met a goodly company of knights riding along the way. And in the company were Sir Lancelot and Sir Safere and Sir Segwarides.

Now these knights were riding toward King Arthur's court for to do honour to Sir Segwarides, that had of late won the prize at a great tournament at Winchester. And for that he bore a great dragon on his shield, ever after was he called the Knight of the Dragon. But Sir Segwarides was inwardly sorrowful, for the lady Iverna his wife, had turned again to Sir Bleoberis, for all that Sir Segwarides had vanquished him at the tournament. Wherefore Sir Segwarides had sworn a great hatred unto the knights of the lineage of Ban. But as at that time he hid it because of Sir Lancelot.

And when the knights saw the men carrying the coffin, they asked whose it might be. Then they told them all that had happed.

'And,' said they, 'we deem that knight had writ his name on the coffin. But we know no letters and cannot read it.'

Then Sir Lancelot bade them set the coffin upon the ground, and he alit from his horse and stooped down to the coffin, and there he read the name of Palomides.

'Alas!' said Sir Lancelot, 'Sir Safere and Sir Segwarides, here is your brother's name writ. And woe is me that so good a knight should come to his death.'

Then all the knights that were there made great sorrow, and Sir Safere and Sir Segwarides above all. And so they took up the coffin and bore it with them to King Arthur. And the king was sore grieved at this tidings.

'But where is the Lord Esclabor become?' said King Arthur, 'For he rode secretly after Sir Palomides. And much I fear for him; for he was an old man and his wounds were not healed.'

But none could answer him at that time. And on the morn came Sir Dinadan to Camelot. And he prayed the king to summon all the knights of the Round Table there for to hear news.

'I will with good will summon those that be here,' said King Arthur, 'but I doubt if there be above forty returned from the quest. And much I misdoubt me of that quest if it were sent of God; for little but sorrow and loss has come of it.'

'Much greater sorrow shall ye have when ye see what I bring,' said Sir Dinadan.

So then came in all the knights that were there, and Sir Dinadan showed them Sir Tristram's sword and shield and told them all that had befallen. And then Sir Lancelot told Sir Dinadan of the death of Sir Palomides. And great was the lamentation that they made for the death of two such knights.

But Sir Dinadan went unto Sir Lancelot and said unto him: 'Are ye sure that Sir Palomides lies within that coffin? For methinks ye opened it not.'

'That is truth,' said Sir Lancelot, 'but his name is upon it, and for why would a man that is a-dying take upon himself another's name?'

'As to that,' said Sir Dinadan, 'who hath heard tell of a dying man that had his coffin so at hand and wrote his name on it? And of all knights living it is not Sir Palomides that would do so. For save if he were driven by envy or love of

Iseult or in the heat of battle he sought no fame for himself.'

And Sir Dinadan said no more as at that time, but he bethought him that he would go in quest of Sir Palomides.

XXIII

The Achievement of the Quest

Now the page that Lord Esclabor had sent unto the Lady Etain rode swiftly upon his way; and when he came to the castle where she dwelt he found saddling of horses and much press of men, and he marvelled greatly what this might be. And so he came where the Lady Etain was, and with her Igraine the Fair. And when the Lady Etain saw him, she said: 'Lo, here is he come that shall lead us to my dear son, Sir Palomides.'

For the Lady Etain had had a dream; and in her dream the Lord Esclabor called upon her for aid, and also Sir Palomides called upon her. And it was so that in her dream, ere she awoke, the voice of the Lord Esclabor grew faint till he called no more; but the voice of Sir Palomides grew ever stronger till at last she awaked. And then she summoned her people and bade them make ready, for she would go upon a journey.

And so she stayed not to hear what the page would say, but mounted her palfrey and bade him lead her to Sir Palomides. But as they rode Igraine drew unto the page and bade him tell her all that had befallen. And when she heard his tale she nigh swooned for sorrow, and scarce might sit upon her horse.

But Etain bade her take heart.

'For,' said she, 'methinks it is I that have the greater sorrow, for the dead call not for succour and it is my Lord and not my son that ceased to call.'

So the Lady Igraine held her peace at that time, and so they rode all of them till they came where Sir Palomides lay. And when Igraine saw him lie so still, she deemed him dead indeed. And she alit from her palfrey and flung herself upon him and wept as though her heart would break.

But the Lady Etain lifted her up and chid her for great sorrow out of measure. And then the Lady Etain searched the wounds of Sir Palomides, and much she marvelled that he was still warm with those great wounds upon him.

'Ah let be, Madam!' cried Igraine the Fair. 'For he is beyond human aid. Leave him in peace and let us make our laments and our prayers, for anon must we bury him.'

'True it is, I wis,' said Etain, 'that he is beyond aid of man. Yet he is not dead, and he is not beyond the aid of God. Therefore we will take him up and bear him gently unto the castle of Carbonek, that peradventure God may have mercy upon him and upon us.'

And as they lifted Sir Palomides, there came the hermit to them. And he told them how he had left the old knight with the coffin when he went into the forest; and when he was come again he found nor knight nor coffin, and knew not what had befallen them.

'Alas!' said Etain. 'Now is my dream true. For never unless he were dead would my Lord have left his dear son. Ah my dear Lord, that on earth I shall no more see! God grant you his peace and to this our child new life!'

And, as they went on their way to Carbonek, there came to them Sir Dinadan and saluted them fair. And either told other their tidings. And then they wit well that it was the

Lord Esclabor that lay dead within the coffin that bore the name of Palomides.

And so on a day they came to Carbonek. And there were Sir Galahad, Sir Bors, Sir Percival, and a great host of people. And it was said that those three knights should carry the Grail out of Logres. And on that day Sir Galahad had healed the maimed King Pellam.

So when they heard these things, then went Sir Dinadan unto the castle to seek Sir Galahad. And he encountered with King Pelles, the Lord of the Castle, and prayed him that he would lead him unto Sir Galahad.

'That may not be,' said King Pelles, 'for now Sir Galahad careth no more for the things of this world nor for the men of this world, save his two companions that will with him go upon this holy quest.'

'That me repenteth,' said Sir Dinadan, 'for holy the quest may be for them that achieve it, but ill enough hath been done by some that went upon it. And I deem the quest shall be no less holy if some of the ill may be set right.'

And then he told King Pelles of all that had befallen Sir Palomides.

'Nonetheless,' said Sir Pelles, 'ye may not come at him. For none may go unto the holy place where he is.'

'Then will I await him here,' said Sir Dinadan, 'for I deem it a shameful thing if holiness may not beget good deeds.'

And in a little time a door opened near the place where they stood, and there came out thereat Sir Galahad, and with him Sir Bors and Sir Percival. And when Sir Dinadan looked upon them, well he wot that Sir Galahad and Sir Percival were no more ware of earthly things. But Sir Bors looked this way and that upon the people. So Sir Dinadan plucked

Sir Bors by the sleeve as he passed and prayed him aid for Sir Palomides.

Then Sir Bors stayed Sir Galahad as he went, and bade Sir Dinadan bring Sir Palomides to that place, and so it was done. And Sir Bors made Sir Galahad to look upon Sir Palomides; and when he saw him he went back into the Holy Place and touched again the spear, as he had done for Sir Pellam, and came again and knelt by Sir Palomides and touched him with the blood of the spear. And when he had prayed long, he rose and said to the Lady Etain: 'Fear no more for thy son. He is now but as one that sleepeth. But when he is awaked, bid him remember the quest that is his own quest and fail not.'

And then Sir Galahad and his companions departed. And then King Pelles made ready a room in the castle, and therein they laid Sir Palomides. And the Lady Etain, and Igraine the Fair, and Sir Dinadan watched beside his bed.

And after seven days Sir Palomides awoke as from sleep, as Sir Galahad had said. And he raised him up upon the bed and looked upon those that watched and asked them how he came there and what place that was. And then they told him all that had befallen. And Sir Palomides marvelled greatly and gave great thanks unto God.

And then the Lady Etain spake to Sir Palomides of his quest, as Sir Galahad had bidden her. And anon Sir Palomides arose and called for his armour, but he was so weak he might not stand. So then it was agreed that he should return to his mother's castle, and there abide till that he might have his strength again. And so thither they returned on the morrow. And when Sir Dinadan had seen Sir Palomides safely bestowed, he returned to King Arthur's Court and told all that had befallen.

So Sir Palomides abode a full year, and his mother and Igraine so tended him that his strength came back to him and he was as a new man. And on a day as he walked in the castle he found Igraine sitting in a window. And he beheld how fair she was and remembered him of his old love for her. And he came softly to her and took her hand and said:

'Lady, too much have ye done for me that am all unworthy. And many things there are that I would say unto thee but as at this time I dare not. Therefore I thank thee from my heart, and take my leave. For I must go to the court of my lord King Arthur, there to try my strength; and then must I go upon the quest. And, an I prosper therein, I will come again.'

'My lord, Sir Palomides,' said Igraine, 'there is nought ye would say unto me that I would not gladly hear. Yet speak or be silent as ye will. And, if it may ease you, I know all the great love that ye bore to La Beale Iseult that is dead, and I would to God for your sake that ye had had better speed of it.'

'Lady,' said Sir Palomides, 'that love came nigh to my undoing. For in love as in war a man must strive to the uttermost or hold off. Much I did to win Queen Iseult, but never enough. And I thank God that of love for her I was cured; and not only for my own sake, but I ceased to trouble her or my lord, Sir Tristram.'

'Why do ye say this to me?' said Igraine.

'To the end that ye may wish me God speed in my quest,' said Sir Palomides, 'that is not only a quest of the Beast Glatisant but of my own soul. Also, an I achieve it, I crave leave to speak further with you.'

'I will await your coming,' said Igraine, 'and I will pray God ever to speed you well.'

So then Sir Palomides took his leave of her and of his

mother, and departed to the court of King Arthur. And at that time the noise grew great about the queen and Sir Lancelot, so that at last the queen did forfend him the Court. So Sir Lancelot rode secretly and lodged him with the hermit, Sir Brastias, that dwelt beside Windsor, till he should have tidings.

Then the queen let make a privy dinner in London unto the knights of the Round Table and all was for to shew outward that she had as great joy in all other knights of the Round Table as she had in Sir Lancelot. And many knights were bidden to that dinner, and among them Sir Palomides and Sir Safere. And there at that dinner Sir Patrise ate of some fruit that was poisoned, and there died. And many that were there accused the queen thereof, and Sir Mador de la Porte, that was cousin to Sir Patrise, appelled the queen of treason.

So on the day appointed that the queen should be condemned save one should be her champion there came Sir Lancelot and overthrew Sir Mador. And thereafter came the lady of the Lake and told how that Sir Pinel le Savage had poisoned an apple for to be avenged on Sir Gawaine for the slaying of his cousin, Sir Lamorak.

Then were the king and queen passing glad; and King Arthur proclaimed many great tournaments, as he used aforetime before the quest. And Sir Palomides essayed his strength therein, and did right valiantly; and ofttimes he bore away the prize.

And on a day there came to him Sir Dinadan and mocked him and said:

'I marvel that the good knight, Sir Galahad, raised you from the dead. For thou art just such another as all these knights that have no thought but to knock each other off their horses. And as aforetime ye were never the best of all because of Sir Tristram, so now Sir Lancelot is better than ye.'

'I try my strength,' said Sir Palomides, 'as ye well know, for that quest that is appointed me.'

'In good truth,' said Sir Dinadan, 'meseemed ye had forgotten. And as for your strength, I never heard tell that the Questing Beast rode upon a horse that ye might smite it down from.'

'Ye say truth,' said Sir Palomides, 'and would that I knew what I must do to that Beast, for never yet could I come at it.'

'Ye never tried,' said Sir Dinadan, 'but in fury and madness, as ye play in jousts. For had ye had the will to endure to the end, well I ween ye had outlasted Sir Tristram in the field, as often ye outdid him at the beginning of a tournament. So also if ye had persevered in your quest of the Beast, long since ye had achieved it.'

'As for that,' said Sir Palomides, 'now I will go again in quest of that Beast. And I warrant me that I will not leave it till I achieve it or else it shall be my death.'

'That is well said,' said Sir Dinadan. 'Now let us see if your deeds shall match your words.'

So then they took leave each of other, and Sir Palomides rode forth upon his quest. And he went into the heart of Logres among the great forests where few men dwelt, for well he wot that the Questing Beast would shun the haunts of men.

And on a day as he lay beside a fountain to rest himself, Sir Palomides heard the sound as of twenty couple of hounds baying, and he wist that the Beast would come to drink at that fountain. Wherefore he withdrew him a little into the forest, and there hid where he might see what would befall.

And anon the Beast came to the fountain and there drank: and as it drank the noise in its belly was stayed. And Sir Palomides watched the Beast, and rushed not in as he did aforetime; for well he wot that that way he might not come at it.

So when the Beast had drunk its fill, it lifted up its head and beheld the sun that was there sunk far to westward, for it was evening. And then the Beast went on its way towards the sun. And the noise in the Beast's belly was stayed for it had well drunken. And Sir Palomides took his horse and rode swiftly after the Beast. And lo, as the sun set, the Beast lay down there where it was to take its rest. And Sir Palomides stayed him near by.

But in a little while the noise of hounds awoke again within the Beast's belly. And thereon the Beast arose again and went on its way. And in the night it went this way and that, and ever Sir Palomides kept as near as he might. But if ever the Beast heard any sound that affrighted it, then it went so swift a pace that the swiftest horse might not overtake it.

And so Sir Palomides rode many days till he and his horse were so weary they scarce might stand. And the Beast was wont to drink at sunrise and midday and sunset, but it seemed to Sir Palomides that it ate not at all and slept but little. And in the day when it had drunk it went ever towards the sun, save an it were affrighted. But in the night it went hither and yon as though with no purpose.

So Sir Palomides him thought that never might he take the Beast by swiftness or by rushing in upon it, but by some stratagem. Yet he was so weary that ofttimes he thought to attack the Beast or else to leave it. But ever he bethought him how oft he had failed through lack of patience and continuance, and he deemed it were better for him to die of weariness on this quest than to fail again or to leave it.

And on a day, as he followed the Beast, the noise of the hounds was grown so great that he wist that the Beast must soon turn to a fountain. And they came to a place of high rocks where he scarce might see the path. And on a sudden his horse fell down under him and there lay. And Sir Palomides voided his horse, and then he saw that his horse was dead. Wit ye well that he was then nigh to despair, for he knew not how he might come by another horse.

So then he left his spear and his shield by the dead horse, for he might not carry them, and so he went after the noise of the Beast on foot. And at first it seemed that the noise drew away from him; but thereafter it grew loud, and he deemed that he was coming up on the Beast.

And then he came to a place where a narrow path led between high rocks with many thorny trees therein. And it seemed that the Beast went slowly for it scarce might pass. And when Sir Palomides deemed that he might go no further for weariness and toil, he beheld where the path ended in a circle of high rocks, within which was a little fountain. And before him was the Beast that went to the fountain. And then Sir Palomides looked up and around him; and he saw that the sun was behind him, and that there was no way out from the fountain save by the path that he had come.

Then Sir Palomides gave a cry and drew his sword, and ran upon the Beast as he might. And when the Beast heard Sir Palomides it turned, and snatched the sword out of his hand with its mouth, and rose up on its hind legs against Sir Palomides as though it would crush him. And Sir Palomides drew his dagger, and struck at the Beast's belly as it rose and there made a great and grimly rent.

And as Sir Palomides stepped back if so he might avoid the Beast, the Beast gave a great cry and fell down upon its side. And out of the rent in its belly came out twenty couple of hounds, more gaunt and grisly than ever he had seen. And they bared their fangs upon Sir Palomides, and truly he thought his end was come. But then they smelled the fountain, and so rushed down to drink. And, as Palomides watched he saw that the hounds drank without measure and stayed not. And so one after other they drank till they burst themselves and so lay dead.

Then Sir Palomides turned to the Questing Beast that lay still there where it had fallen. And he deemed the Beast was dead, save that its eyes were open and ever it gazed upon him. And as Sir Palomides looked him seemed that he gazed into his own eyes. And he wot not what he must do.

So as he was forspent[1] and weary he took a great corded rope that he had borne with him, and he tied one end around the neck of the Beast. And then he made fast the rope in the midst of a great tree that was by the fountain. And the other end he tied round his own body. And then Sir Palomides fell down beside the tree as it were in a swoon, and so fell on sleep.

[1] exhausted.

XXIV

The Duke of Provence

AND so Sir Palomides slept for three days and three nights. And on the fourth day at the rising of the sun he deemed he heard one call 'Palomides! Palomides!' And so he awoke and got up and looked thereas he had left the Beast. But of the Beast he could see no trace. Only there lay near at hand an old woman with a rope round her neck, that stretched her hands towards him and cried to him by name.

Then he went unto the old woman and loosed the rope from about her neck. And he was greatly astonished how she came there and what had befallen the Beast.

'Marvel not, Sir Palomides,' said she, 'for I was the Questing Beast that thou hast slain in delivering me from the evils that thou sawest as hounds. And from my heart I thank thee. For many years have I carried them in my belly for the sin of my mother. And ever was I doomed to flee from noble knights until one that was steadfast to the end and would not leave my quest should deliver me. Now is my questing done. And I prithee take me upon thy shoulders and bear me forth of this place until we find an holy man that may baptize me, that so I may die and my soul have rest. And in truth that shall be small toil for thee after all that thou hast endured for my sake.'

So Sir Palomides took her up upon his shoulders. Also he

took again his sword that he found near by. And he went by the narrow path among the rocks until they were forth of that place. And easy seemed the way to him after the grief and the toil that he had in entering it.

And when he had gone but a little way in the forest there stood before him an old man that leaned upon a long staff. And he said to Sir Palomides:

'Welcome, Sir Palomides, good knight, that faithfully have achieved your quest. And soon shall ye have your reward. For I am Blaise that aforetime counselled thee. Now bear this woman to my dwelling here at hand that I may baptize her. And then shall ye hear what ye must do.'

So Sir Palomides bore the old woman to the hut. And there the hermit Blaise did baptize her. And thereafter she gave up the ghost, praising God and giving thanks for Sir Palomides. And so Blaise and Sir Palomides buried her there in the forest. And thereafter Sir Palomides abode with Blaise till he should hear tidings. For so Blaise commanded him.

And on a day Sir Palomides was awaked by the neighing of horses, and he arose up to see what this might mean. And ere he could go forth, Blaise stood beside him, and said:

'Tell me, Sir Palomides, ye that have seen marvels, what would ye that I should show unto you? Would ye see Queen Iseult an I bring her forth from the dead?'

'Nay, Sir,' said Sir Palomides, 'I would not see Queen Iseult save she had need of my service. For well I know now that the love I had for her was but lust of the eyes, and lust of fame for the deeds I might do for her sake. And as for her, I wit well that the best service I might do her is to be away from her. Yet greatly I hope that she may find in her heart to pardon me where she now is.'

'Then what marvel would ye that I show unto you?' said Blaise.

'I would no marvel,' said Sir Palomides, 'nor any raised from the dead. But one mortal woman there is that hath endured longer for me than I for the Questing Beast. And if I might see her again I would ask nor marvels nor miracles.'

'Then go ye forth,' said Blaise, 'for ye need not help from me to win a mortal woman. Though peradventure there is still one service that I may do for you.'

Then went Sir Palomides forth to see what was toward. And he beheld horses that stood about the hut and the men that tended them. And when he came to the hut, lo there he found his mother and Igraine the Fair that Blaise had summoned thither. Wit you well that Sir Palomides rejoiced greatly thereat and so did the Lady Etain and the damsel Igraine. And when each had greeted other, then the Lady Etain told Sir Palomides how strife had broken out at King Arthur's court because of Sir Lancelot and the queen, and because of the jealousy and hatred that Sir Gawaine's brethren bare to Lancelot.

'Then thither must I hie me,' said Sir Palomides, 'for I will be by the side of my lord, Sir Lancelot, an he be in peril. Yet first I have a thing to do an I may.'

Then turned he him to Igraine the Fair, and said:

'My lady, the quest I was upon is ended. And well I wot it was for love of you and by your prayers that it is ended well. And now, my lady and my true love, an ye be willing, I would ask the holy hermit, Blaise, to do that last service that he hath promised me, and to marry us two here that we may part no more.'

'I will well,' said Igraine.

So then did Blaise wed Sir Palomides and Igraine the Fair there in the forest. And on the morn he blessed them, and so they and the Lady Etain and their company departed for the court of King Arthur.

So when they were come there, Sir Palomides found his brethren, Sir Safere and Sir Segwarides, and the most part of the Round Table that were left were there gathered. Then was it told him that that night Sir Lancelot had been taken in the queen's room by knights that lay in wait. And Sir Lancelot had come forth and had slain the most part of those knights and so escaped. And now was the Round Table all at strife.

And when the evening was come, then came Sir Bors and Sir Ector and others of the lineage of Ban to find what knights would cleave unto Sir Lancelot, and what knights would be against him. And Sir Palomides and Sir Safere held with Sir Lancelot. But Sir Segwarides would not for hatred of Sir Bleoberis. So then Sir Lancelot and all his party withdrew them until they should learn what the king would do.

And on a day it was told unto Sir Lancelot that that day the queen should be burnt in a field hard by Carlisle. And King Arthur had bidden all his knights to come armed into the field where the queen should have her judgment.

And so a great company was gathered unto the field. But Sir Lancelot hid him and those that were with him in a wood hard by and he sent one to espy what time the queen should go unto her death. And anon, as Sir Lancelot had warning, he and they that were with him rode suddenly out of the wood and rescued the queen by force. And in the rushing and the hurling there were slain full many a noble knight; and amongst them Sir Segwarides; and Sir Gareth and Sir Gaheris that were brethren to Sir Gawaine.

And then Sir Lancelot and his company bore the queen to Joyous Garde. And there many great lords and noble knights drew unto him. And Sir Gawaine was wood wroth at the death of his brethren and ever he stirred up the king to make war upon Sir Lancelot. And so the king gathered his host and laid siege about Sir Lancelot where he lay in Joyous Garde.

But Sir Lancelot held him ever within the castle, for in no wise would he fight against King Arthur. And Sir Gawaine made many men to blow upon Sir Lancelot, and so all at once they called him false and recreant knight.

But when Sir Bors, Sir Ector de Maris and Sir Lionel heard this outcry, they called unto them Sir Palomides, and all they went unto Sir Lancelot and said:

'My lord, wit you well we have great scorn of the great rebuke that we have heard Sir Gawaine say unto you; wherefore we pray you, and charge you as ye will have our service, keep us no longer within these walls. For we let you wit plain we would ride into the field and do battle with them. For ye fare as a man that were afeared; yet all their fair speech will not avail you, for wit you well Sir Gawaine will never suffer you to accord with King Arthur. And therefore fight for your life and right, an ye dare!'

'Then must I needs unto battle,' said Sir Lancelot.

And so on the morrow Sir Lancelot's fellowship came out at the three gates in good array. Sir Lionel came in the foremost battle, and Sir Lancelot came in the middle, and Sir Bors came out at the third gate. And ever Sir Lancelot charged all his knights in any wise to save King Arthur and Sir Gawaine. And for that cause, though Sir Bors and Sir Palomides and Sir Safere and many other noble knights did many worshipful deeds yet they could not put the king's party to the worse. And then either party withdrew them to repose them and bury their dead.

And so on the morn the battle was joined again and there was much slaughter on both parties. Then his brethren prayed Sir Lancelot to do his pain and fight as they did.

'For,' said they, 'we see that ye forbear and spare, and that doth us much harm. And therefore, we pray you, spare not your enemies no more than they do you.'

'Alas,' said Sir Lancelot, 'I have no heart to fight against my lord, Arthur, for ever meseemeth I do not as me ought to do.'

'My lord,' said Sir Palomides, 'though ye spare them, never so much all this day they will not you thank; and, if they may get you at avail,[1] ye are but a dead man.'

So then Sir Lancelot understood that they said him truth. And then he strained himself more than he did aforetime; and, so by evening time Sir Lancelot's party the better stood. And thereafter they upon the king's party were not so orgulous[2] as they were aforetime to do battle. Yet ever Sir Gawaine rode about and cried shame upon Sir Lancelot, and ever Sir Lancelot forebore him.

And when Sir Palomides saw that, he rode to Sir Gawaine ere Sir Lancelot might let him, and bade him defend himself. And so they two came together like thunder, and there Sir Palomides smote down Sir Gawaine horse and man to the earth. And then Sir Palomides alit to do battle on foot. And Sir Gawaine arose, and drew his sword and came running upon Sir Palomides; and then Sir Palomides struck him such a blow that he fell grovelling to the earth, and scarce might move.

So then Sir Palomides went to Sir Gawaine and raced off his

[1] at their mercy.   [2] proudly confident.

helm. And then he unbuckled Sir Gawaine's armour, and so stripped Sir Gawaine to his shirt. And Sir Gawaine deemed he would be slain. And then he cried aloud and said: 'Who art thou that so dishonourest me? Now, an thou wouldst slay me, make an end.'

'Not so,' said Sir Palomides, 'albeit a shameful death ye deserve. For I obey the word of my lord, Sir Lancelot. Know then that I am Sir Palomides that ye would have foully slain. And now, thou murderer of noble knights, I scorn to slay thee. But I will send thee back to my lord King Arthur in such guise that all men may know thy shame.'

Then Sir Palomides took Sir Gawaine in his arms, and set him upon his horse backward, and so bound him upon his horse. And then he smote the horse so that it ran back with Sir Gawaine to the King's host. And Sir Palomides mounted his horse and rode back to Joyous Garde. Wit ye well that all the knights with Sir Lancelot were right glad that Sir Gawaine was so discomfited and the name of Sir Lancelot avenged.

And on the morrow there came the Bishop of Rochester. And the Pope had given him bulls under lead and sent them to the king, charging him upon pain of interdicting of all England that he take his queen again and accord with Sir Lancelot. And so it was done. Yet Sir Gawaine would not leave the king to be accorded save that Sir Lancelot was banished out of Logres.

So Sir Lancelot and all his company shipped at Cardiff and sailed unto Benwick. And at that time Sir Lancelot and his kin were lords of all France. And so Sir Lancelot stablished his lands, and then he advanced all his noble knights. And Sir Palomides, he made him Duke of Provence, and Sir Safere he made him Duke of Languedoc.

So then Sir Palomides took his leave of Sir Lancelot, and rode into Provence with Igraine the Fair. And wit you well right glad was Sir Palomides to be at peace; and nobly he ruled his lands many years, and his people loved him.